faith
and
FINANCE

Financial Planning with a Faith Factor
A 12 lesson practical study on money management

Prepared by the Stewardship Department of the North American Division of Seventh-day Adventists

This book was Edited by G. Edward Reid

Design/Layout by 316 Creative

PRINTED IN U.S.A.

12 11 10 09 08   5 4 3 2 1

ISBN 0-9711134-7-5

CONTENTS

Authors' Introduction

Congratulations! You are holding in your hands some life-changing information. We know because we have experienced it. We frequently hear, "Why didn't someone tell us this before now?" We all must deal with money management. How much better it is if you can go for help to someone with experience. That is just what you are getting with this material—experience—a lot of it!

Gordon Botting, Dick Hanson, Ben Maxson, and Ed Reid have a combined life experience of over 200 years! Yes, we all have grey hair. We all have already raised our families. Together we have been teaching Christian principles of money management for a combined total of over 70 years.

Like many of you, we received our education at a time when very few schools offered courses in money management—let alone life management. But, sensing a need for better personal money management and a desire to share this information with others, we have all, at different times, taken additional training—including seminars and certification programs—that have shaped our lives and ministries. We all are committed Christians and were basically familiar with the Biblical encouragement toward financial faithfulness. What we needed was someone or something to organize what we basically already knew into a practical, easy-to-understand format. We believe that, providentially, we all were individually and at different times led to complete the certification program designed and delivered by the late Larry Burkett and his team in what was then known as Christian Financial Concepts. We feel blessed to have a continuing relationship with Howard Dayton and the new Crown Financial Ministries. In addition, we all have been involved and certified by the Christian Stewardship Association.

Since those early days we all have conducted hundreds of Stewardship and Money Management seminars, printed books, and presented radio and television programs on money management. What makes this material unique is not our degrees and graduate education or the books we have written and read. This material is unique and life changing because we are sharing what we have encountered in our walks with God and the interesting experiences we have had and been told by our students over the years. To our knowledge, there is nothing else quite like this material available that combines in such a unique way the Biblical principles of money management, the practical lessons of life, and proven academic information on this topic.

We have prayed in advance that each person or family that goes through this material will be blessed beyond their expectations and will in the end be a candidate to hear the words of our Lord, "Well done, good and faithful servant."

—Gordon Botting, Dick Hanson, Ben Maxson, and Ed Reid

Editor's Preface

This book came about in a unique manner. As I presented money management seminars in churches and camp meetings across the North American Division, people would frequently ask if there was additional material I could recommend as a follow-up to my presentations. Families wanted data that was Biblically based and yet had the practical information needed to manage family finances in today's world. I was familiar with most of the money management material that has been written from a Christian perspective. I felt we could and should produce study material that would outline basic Biblical principles and also include practical application all in one book. This book is the result of that dream.

Committees and groups are good for brainstorming and idea generation but not so much, as we found out, for writing a book. I asked three of my ministry associates, men of commitment and experience, to join with me in some planning sessions for the development of the book. Their names are listed in the Author's Introduction. We met together for planning and prayer on four or five occasions of two days each. It was quite a commitment of time. During our planning sessions we came up with twelve topics that we felt must be addressed in the book. They are the current chapter titles. We each took several topics, some more than others, and developed a basic outline and did some writing on that topic.

When I started putting the chapters together I discovered that we all had come at the material with a different format. Some of the material was in outline form, some in narrative, and some in prose – but all good basic material. In the editing process, which has taken me about 3 years, I have tried to glean all of the good ideas and illustrations from each team member and also keep up with current information and statistics. The reader will note that on occasion I have used the editorial "we" and other times I have used "I" as the originator of a thought or idea. Some of my ideas and illustrations are unique to me or my family, so in those cases I have used the personal pronoun "I". I hope this change of singular and plural is not too distracting to you.

For two reasons, all four of us as authors have agreed not to receive any royalty or financial remuneration for our work on this project. The first is that we believe that God has blessed us with the opportunities and experiences that we have had and therefore, for the sake of stewardship education, wish to make our contribution in kind. The second is that we want the material to be made available at an affordable price for all families. Any profit over production costs will be retained by the North American Division Stewardship Department to be used for the production of additional training materials.

I wish to thank Gordon Botting, Dick Hanson, and Ben Maxson for their contributions to this work. And special thanks to my administrative assistant, Lori Bryan, whose work and counsel has been very valuable. It has been our prayer that this book would strengthen Christian families both spiritually and financially.

– G Edward Reid, Editor
Stewardship Director
North American Division of Seventh-day Adventists

Getting Started

Welcome to the **Faith & Finance** Bible study program. We believe you will be pleased with what you learn in this study. These materials will help you discover and integrate Biblical principles into your life. The three primary objectives in this study are to help you:

- identify and explore Biblical principles for dealing with money and material possessions;
- choose practical ways for integrating God into how you manage His money; and,
- make Biblical Christianity more real and practical.

The **Faith & Finance** material has been prepared with 12 chapters or lessons and can be studied in a variety of ways. You may do an individual study if you are a motivated self-starter, or you may participate with a small group at church or in a home. The advantages of the small group format are the opportunity to review the material after studying it and to glean ideas and learn from others as you interact together.

Each lesson will present a memory text from the Bible. So that you can learn the same one that your group members are learning, we will suggest the New King James Version and will print it at the beginning of each lesson.

The lesson then will continue with a reading section that will introduce the topic and lay down the principle(s) for study. Following the chapter reading will come a Bible study and, in most cases, a practical application section with forms that have been prepared to help you see your current situation and/or make plans for your future.

You will receive the greatest benefit from this material by taking each lesson seriously. Learn the memory text, read the lesson, and prepare the study material. At each step pray that God will guide you and open your understanding for a lasting application in your life.

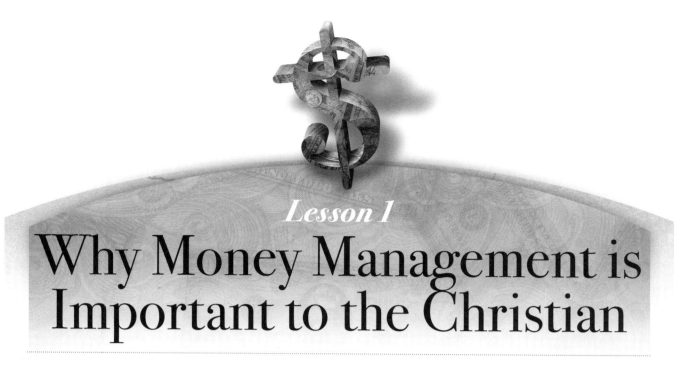

Why Money Management is Important to the Christian

Memory Text: Matthew 6:33

"But seek first the kingdom of God and His righteousness,
and all these things shall be added to you."

Money and Value

What is it about money that is so alluring, so tempting? Stop and think about it for just a moment. How do you feel when the bills are due and you don't have the money you need to pay them? Then, how do you feel when you cash your surprise birthday check and you have a crisp $100 bill in your pocket? There is a strange sense of security when you have enough money. With enough money you can purchase whatever you want. Or at least that is often the thought: "Just think of what we could do if we just had a little more money!"

Pause for a moment and consider how much our society focuses its attention around money—how to get more, how to invest it, and how to spend it. Money is equated with success and power, with recognition and position, with accomplishment and importance. On the other hand, the lack of money is often seen as failure and weakness.

God and Money

Have you ever thought of trying to live without money? Many people in the world do. But it would be rather difficult in our society. On the other hand, have you ever thought of living without God? What if you had to choose between money and God?

Jesus contrasts the competing power of money with God by stating, *"No one can serve two masters; for either he will hate the one and love the other, or else he will be loyal to the one and despise the other. You cannot serve God and mammon [money, wealth, riches]"* (Matthew 6:24). There are few places in Scripture where God makes such a direct comparison. Yet the competition is very real. Money competes for our interest, our time, and our energy. It easily distracts us from more important priorities.

Two-thirds of Jesus' parables deal with money and material possessions or our attitude toward them. There are well over two thousand Biblical references that deal with this topic, while there are only about five hundred verses on prayer and fewer than five hundred on faith. Obviously, God thinks knowledge about money is very important.

Money plays a crucial role in our lives. We cannot deal without it. Even God's church has to deal with money. So, the issue facing us is not whether or not we will deal with money, but rather the level of importance or priority it has in our lives. It is a matter of what we love—a matter of where we will focus our passion.

What is your passion? What motivates and drives your life? Though these are not easy questions to answer, they reflect on two contrasting forces that shape our life and character.

Jesus said, *"And you shall love the Lord your God with all your heart, with all your soul, with all your mind, and with all your strength" (Mark 12:30).* And Paul warned us in writing to his young friend Timothy, *"For the love of money is a root of all kinds of evil, for which some have strayed from the faith in their greediness, and pierced themselves through with many sorrows" (1 Timothy 6:10).*

Starting at the Beginning

How do we deal with money, since we cannot get away from it? The starting point should be where God starts, Genesis 1:1, *"In the beginning God created the heavens and the earth."* The very first thing that the Bible establishes about God is that He is the Creator of Heaven and Earth, and this forms the foundation for everything else the Bible says about Him, about who we are, and about how we should relate to Him.

The fact that God is the Creator of Heaven and Earth means that everything belongs to Him. This is precisely why David wrote, *"The earth is the Lord's, and all its fullness, the world and those who dwell therein. For He has founded it upon the seas, and established it upon the waters" (Psalms 24:1, 2).* Stop and think of what would change if this concept of God's ownership became a reality in our thinking. How would our priorities be different? Would we choose to use our time differently? Would we

place greater importance on relationships? Would we give God more time? Would we change the way we think or the way we act?

We cannot truly accept God as Owner unless we learn to trust Him. Only when we experience the treasure of God's love and grace can we deal correctly with material possessions—our treasures. Without the security of a personal walk with God, we will seek security on our own. In this materialistic world, we will search for security in money or in that which money can buy. But regardless of how much we have, security eludes us, for money is always temporary and what it buys rapidly wastes away. The wise man said, *"He who loves silver will not be satisfied with silver, nor he who loves abundance, with increase. This also is vanity" (Ecclesiastes 5:10).*

The true value of money only can be seen in the context of God's kingdom. Money is only a tool or symbol. Thirty pieces of silver purchased Judas' betrayal of his Master (See Matthew 26:15; 27:3-9). Two mites demonstrated the relationship of faith and trust of a lonely widow whose only support was a God she had learned to worship (See Mark 12:42-44). The pieces of silver were cast back at the feet of those who had rejected the Savior. The two mites, however, continue to stimulate endless gifts of grace and love. Money we invest in this world ultimately passes away. What we invest in God's kingdom stores up treasures for eternity.

Does this mean that we should give all our money to God? Of course not! It already belongs to Him. What it means is that we recognize that every part of life becomes an act of worship as we manage God's assets in the different dimensions of His kingdom. For example, tithe becomes recognition of who God is and who we are; offerings become acts of worship and praise, celebrating experienced grace and the wonder of a God who provides for all our needs; and what we invest in supplying the needs of our family is also an act of worship as we care for those God has put in our immediate trust.

The key issue here is one of attitude. One approach says that we are the owners. The other joyfully confesses our dependence on God as the Owner of all. Therefore, if we do not recognize God as the Owner of the money He places in our hands to manage, then that money begins to own us! This is why God makes a contrast in the context of whom or what we serve. *"You cannot serve both God and money"* (Matthew 6:24).

So, how we manage our money influences our relationship with God. Our checkbook, credit card or bank statements are a constant diary telling the stories of how we make God the priority of our lives. Do we allow our meaning and security to come into our walk with God, or do we seek them in our ability to accumulate and use the wealth of material possessions for our own purposes? Who or what will be god in our life? Choose today! What has won the passion of our heart? Is it money? Or, is it God?

The glorious reality is that when we accept Christ, we become part of a new kingdom, a new reality. We are part of His family. We are not trying to work our way into the kingdom. We are not trying to earn the throne. We are already on the throne. We are in Christ. The rest of life is simply living out stewardship. Unfortunately, many have come to think of stewardship as simply a means to get people to give more to support the church. This book is designed to open a window so that we can see with our own eyes the Biblical principles of money management.

The Gospel and Lordship

We begin in view of the cross and how the concept of Lordship influences stewardship. True worship begins with and is based on a relationship with Jesus, intimately knowing Jesus as Savior and Lord. This is why the gospel is the foundation for stewardship. Without the experience of the gospel, stewardship becomes simply a form of spiritual slavery—just another way of perpetrating a performance-based religion and life.

The content of salvation is what we receive when we accept Jesus as Savior. He promises to come to us through the Holy Spirit (John 14:16-20) that we may be transformed and *"be strengthened with might through His Spirit in the inner man, that Christ may dwell in your hearts*

through faith" (Ephesians 3:16, 17). Jesus gives us His righteousness. He forgives us and makes us a new creation (2 Corinthians 5:17). When we receive Christ, He brings the power of God into the human heart, and we live from the very throne of God (Ephesians 2:6). All of this is included in Christ when we accept Him. The very life we live is lived in Him (Galatians 2:20).

The consequence of salvation produces a life of discipleship and obedience. One cannot have Christ dwelling within and remain the same. God promises to give us a new heart and a new spirit (Ezekiel 36:26, 27). He promises to replace our heart of stone with a heart of flesh and to put His Spirit in our hearts. He further states that He will cause us to walk in His principles. Paul presents the same concept when he states that it is God who will work in us both to will and to do (Philippians 2:13). The natural result of experiencing Jesus as Savior also leads us to share with others what we have experienced.

So how do we experience this dynamic salvation? There is no way to dissect the mystery of grace. The work of the Holy Spirit in a sinner's heart can be experienced but never described in full detail or understanding. Every part of this dynamic experience of salvation is by faith and choice of will. We choose to believe that what God says is true, and we choose to act—allowing God to work through us.

This brings us back full circle to stewardship as the integration of the saving relationship with Christ into every area of life. In the past you may have felt that Lordship was just obeying God. Now we can all understand that Lordship is accepting God as Him at His word. And choosing to accept Him is the only way to work out His will in our lives.

Because of our sinful nature and the influence of sin all around us, each day we must choose to reaffirm our relationship with God. Each day we must accept His gift of grace. Each day we must surrender to His indwelling Lordship. Each day we must abandon ourselves to Him to be controlled and empowered through the living presence of Christ. Only then will obedience be a joyful experience of seeing His power at work in the midst of our struggles.

This is how tithing becomes an experience of joy—reflecting on our relationship with God. When we bring this intimate partnership into the material area of life, we realize that everything we are and have belongs to Him. Joyfully we worship Him with tithe and offerings, reminding our own hearts of who He is. Only the dynamic experience of salvation can move tithing, or any other part of lifestyle stewardship, out of the drudgery and slavery of legalism and into the joyful life of grace.

Sacrifice and Giving

Sacrifice is not so much what we give up— "givin' 'til it hurts"—but rather, what we offer to God in recognition of who He is (Creator of Heaven and Earth and Owner of everything) and who we are in relationship to Him. Worship was the context for the first Biblical sacrifice. Cain and Abel brought their offerings to God. One was rejected and the other accepted. The difference lay in their attitudes toward giving. Cain, full of pride, chose his own way; Abel, on the other hand, willingly followed God's instructions. *"By faith Abel offered to God a more excellent sacrifice than Cain, through which he obtained witness that he was righteous, God testifying of his gifts; and through it he being dead still speaks"* (Hebrews 11:4).

In this sacrifice of obedience lies the foundation for the entire concept: What we give to God, and how we give, reflects an internal attitude toward God. We find the same true meaning of sacrifice in God's rejection of King Saul and his offerings. His offering of animals (from the Amalekites) was unacceptable because of His attitude of rebellion against God's direct instructions. *"Has the Lord as great delight in burnt offerings and sacrifices, as in obeying the voice of the Lord? Behold, to obey is better than sacrifice, and to heed than the fat of rams. For rebellion is as the sin of witchcraft, and stubbornness is as iniquity and idolatry. Because you have rejected the word of the Lord, He has also rejected you from being king"* (1 Samuel 15:22, 23).

In exploring sacrifice as worship, we discover powerful principles that can help us transform our lives into anthems of praise to our Creator God. The first sacrifice was offered in the Garden of Eden. Sin had destroyed the relationship between man and God. Shame had darkened the human heart for the first time. And in the shadows of eternity, God met the nakedness of guilt and shame with the symbolic covering of animal skins. For the first time, an innocent life was sacrificed because of a sinner's guilt. Humanity was banned from Eden. Yet the restoration of Eden was assured in the promise of another sacrifice: *"And I will put enmity between you and the woman, and between your seed and her Seed; He shall bruise your head, and you shall bruise His heel"* (Genesis 3:15). Calvary made that promise an historical reality. God's heel was bruised and the bonds of sin were broken.

Sacrifice for God meant the Innocent One dying so that the guilty one could live. For us, sacrifice must mean surrender, death in Him, and rebirth to a life of praise and worship. For God, it meant loss and pain to restore His creation. For us, it means resolution of our pain—death to sin and birth to His life and power.

The implications of salvation shatter the powerless stereotypes of cultural Christianity. In Christ, life becomes worship (Romans 12:1). As Creator and Redeemer, God owns everything, and we are simply managers of God's property. We acknowledge that relationship when we offer ourselves to Him. When we sacrifice anything, we are merely returning to the original Owner— recognizing what He has done in lifting us from sin to His very throne (Ephesians 2:6). Thus we really give up nothing but our sinful selves when we offer anything to God in worship.

For the Christian then, there can be no pain in giving, or in any other activity that is traditionally termed "sacrifice." Pain in our giving only indicates our continued claim to ownership where the sense of sacrifice as loss perverts worship.

Acknowledging the majesty of God as Creator of Heaven and Earth, we invite you to commit yourself to God. On the authority of God's Word, and from the testimony of millions of people who have already done so, you can be assured that your life will be blessed. The practical material to follow in this book will continue to explore in more detail the Biblical Principles of money management having first established the foundation of God's ownership and the role of the Gospel as starting points to build upon.

Assignment for this lesson:

1. Pray for your small group members by name.
2. Pray that God will grant you His wisdom as you study and apply the material.
3. Memorize the Bible text for this lesson.
4. Complete the daily assignments.
5. Complete the "Lordship and Lifestyle" form.

Worksheet Explanation and Guidelines

Following the narrative and instructional portion of each lesson there will be worksheets for you as participants to complete. There are also several forms for you to complete. This is not "busy work." We believe that in order for you to see the true Biblical basis for the principles found in this book, each reader must get into the word of God personally to make the connection.

Note this example:

Read and Reflect on Proverbs 3:5-10.

Why does God request that we honor Him with our possessions and put Him first?

_____

_____

_____

When you see an exercise like this it is time to take your Bible and prayerfully consider the message of this passage and answer the questions that relate to the passage. You should respond and write down in your own words what this means to you. Frequently, the answer is in the text itself. You might note that God asks us to put Him first because He is the Creator and Owner of everything. Or, because He wants to bless the rest that we manage. Or, because He wants to be our partner in the management of the resources He has entrusted to us. Or, He wants us to develop trust in Him and look to Him for wisdom and direction.

If you are using the Faith and Finance material as the basis of a small group study, you can keep anything that is confidential to yourself and not share it with the members of your group. But in these Bible references that are given following most lessons, your group leader will invite you to share your ideas with the group and invite discussion on each passage. As you begin each class study session the group leader will invite the participants to pray together for specific needs of the group and requests that come to the group's attention. Then the leader will give a brief overview of the lesson sometimes by way of a Power Point presentation. Finally the leader will ask for your participation in reciting the memory text and in the worksheet review.

The forms that are filled out by each participant will remain confidential. However, if you have questions regarding how to fill out the forms or what use should be made of them, your leader will be willing to assist you.

It is to your advantage to complete all of the worksheets and forms. The more you put into the lessons, the more you will get out. We pray that the material will instruct and inspire you for the glory of God

Why Money Management is Important to the Christian

Memory Verse: Matthew 6:33

"But seek first the kingdom of God and His righteousness,
and all these things shall be added to you."

PRAYER TIME:

Make a list of those in your group who have asked for special prayer needs this week and pray for them each day.

_____

_____

_____

Pray also for God's wisdom and blessing as you develop your financial plan.

STUDY TIME:

Day One

Read and reflect on Genesis 1:1, 26-28.

1. What do these verses say about God, and what do they say about us as human beings? _____

_____

_____

_____

2. According to this passage, what is God's role in the affairs of this world, and what is our role? _____

_____

_____

_____

Read and reflect on Psalms 24:1, 2; Deuteronomy 10:14; Psalms 50:10-12; Haggai 2:8; 1 Chronicles 29:10-14.

3. According to these passages, what does God own? _____

_____

_____

4. What are the implications of the above passages for how we should deal with material possessions?

_____

_____

Day Two

Read and reflect on Mark 12:30 and Romans 12:1-2.

1. What are the implications of loving God supremely as described in Mark 12:30? _____

_____

2. What does it mean to offer ourselves to God? _____

_____

_____

3. In what ways do we conform to this world? _____

_____

_____

Read and reflect on 1 Corinthians 10:31 and Colossians 3:17.

4. Where should the honor and glory be in our actions? _____

_____

_____

5. What does it mean to do everything "in the name of the Lord?" _____

_____

_____

6. How would things change in our lives if we applied the principles from these passages? _____

_____

_____

Day Three

Read and reflect on Matthew 25:14-30 and Luke 16:1-12.

1. What lessons can we gain from these parables? _____
   _____
   _____

2. What talents or resource has God entrusted to you? _____
   _____
   _____

3. How does the way we deal with worldly wealth reflect our trustworthiness? _____
   _____
   _____
   _____
   _____
   _____

Day Four

Read and reflect on Matthew 6:19-24.

1. What does it mean to serve money or "mammon"? _____
   _____
   _____
   _____

2. In what ways can money become our master? _____
   _____
   _____
   _____

3. How do we choose to serve God over money? _____
   _____
   _____
   _____
   _____

Day Five

Read and reflect on Philippians 4:13, 19 and 2 Peters 1:3, 4.

1. What conclusions can you draw from these passages? _____
_____
_____

2. What resources do you currently need from God? _____
_____
_____

Read and reflect on Ezekial 36:26-27 and 2 Corinthians 5:17.

3. What areas of your life has God made new, and how do you see Him working in those around you?
_____
_____
_____
_____

Day Six

Answer these questions based on concepts from this lesson.

1. Is the idea of "Lordship" new to you? What could it mean to your life? _____
_____
_____
_____
_____

2. God says He can provide for our needs. What evidence do we have that He can actually do this?
_____
_____
_____
_____
_____

3. How would you explain being "in partnership with God?"

_____

_____

_____

_____

_____

4. What is the role of the Holy Spirit in this relationship with God? _____

_____

_____

_____

_____

_____

5. Would you like to invite God into your life through His Holy Spirit every day? _____

_____

_____

_____

_____

_____

6. Complete form #1 (following page) as you complete this lesson.

Lordship and Lifestyle

1. How would you describe your present understanding of God being the Lord of your life? _____

_____

_____

_____

_____

_____

_____

_____

2. Jot down a few notes as to how you feel about God being involved so personally in your life. _____

_____

_____

_____

_____

_____

_____

_____

3. Are you ready to invite God to be Lord of your life? If so write your commitment here in the form of a

short prayer. Lord I want….. _____

_____

_____

_____

_____

_____

_____

_____

_____

_____

Planning for the Cycle of Life

Memory Text: Proverbs 3:9, 10

"Honor the Lord with your possessions, and with the firstfruits of all you increase; so your barns will be filled with plenty, and your vats will overflow with new wine."

As discussed in Chapter 1, stewardship and Lordship are quite inclusive of all of life. And as Christians we have the responsibility and opportunity to be stewards in many areas. For example, healthful living is really just stewardship of our bodies which are the temple of God (1 Corinthians 3:16, 17). But we are also stewards of the gospel (1 Corinthians 4:1, 2), stewards of our time, stewards of our talents and abilities—our God-given gifts—and stewards of this earth. But for the purposes of this book, while keeping the big picture of stewardship in mind, we will focus primarily on the stewardship of our resources—the Biblical principles of money management.

Personal financial planning is designed to help you obtain the things you need and enhance your enjoyment of life—not the opposite. Jesus said, *"I have come that they may have life, and that they may have it more abundantly"* (John 10:10). Too often, however, people make purchases without considering the financial consequences. Some people shop compulsively, creating financial

difficulties for themselves and their families. Living expenses and other financial obligations should be kept in a spending plan. Spending less than you earn is a basic and necessary step in the journey to achieve long-term financial security. Using a well-conceived spending plan will help you stay within your income while you save and invest for the future. The main source of financial difficulties is overspending.

Financial planners generally encourage clients to consider a broad view when preparing an estate plan. This plan includes planning for education and career decisions, for earning and accumulation decisions, for conservation and saving decisions, and for retirement, distribution, and returning-to-God decisions. For those individuals and families who are willing to work though this process, with mid-course corrections as needed, life will move beyond mere existence to a more pleasant and stress-free experience and a preparation for the life to come.

In this chapter we will establish the foundation for our financial plan by determining where we stand now and outlining the most common goals that are set by people who are seeking financial freedom and are desirous of being financially faithful to God. The Bible says that we should know the state of our business affairs. *"Be diligent to know the state of your flocks, and attend to your herds; for riches are not forever, nor does a crown endure to all generations"* (Proverbs 27:23, 24). In an agrarian society, it was important to know the state of their flocks. In a monetary society and economy, it is just as important to know the state of our finances.

The Balance Sheet

The most useful tool that can be used to determine the state of your personal or family finance is the balance sheet. By using this tool, you can fairly quickly see how things stand as far as your finances are concerned. Every person and family is different as far as income, expenses, and management abilities are concerned. With this in mind, you should use the basic balance sheet as a guideline, using only the lines that are personally relevant and adding lines that are unique to you. The results are not to be shared with others but only for your benefit so you will "know the state of your flocks."

In the worksheet assignment for this lesson, you will have the opportunity to complete a balance sheet. This will provide you with information that you can use to see what your needs are and which areas of your financial picture need tweaking.

Financial Goals

Many people and families don't really have a financial plan and simply live from paycheck to paycheck, paying the bills that squeak the loudest. This ends up being an existence lifestyle that leads many to despair. It is very appropriate that a couple sit down together, ideally early in their relationship, and establish short and long-range goals for their financial situation and then develop a plan to reach their goals.

Long-term goals should be planned in coordination with short-term and intermediate ones. For example, saving for a down payment to buy a house is a short-term goal that can be a foundation for a long term goal: owning your own home.

In addition to being defined by your family situation—married or single, with or without children, etc.—you are also defined by your values. Your values also shape your goals. Your values are the ideals and principles that you consider correct, desirable, and important. This is especially significant to the Christian. *"Therefore, whether you eat or drink, or whatever you do, do all to the glory of God"* (1 Corinthians 10:31). Values have a direct influence on such decisions as spending now versus saving for the future or continuing your education versus getting a job.

Education and Career Choice

While many factors affect daily living habits and financial choices, your employment situation probably affects them the most. Your income level, business associates, and available leisure time are a direct result of the work you do. Studies show that more education increases your potential earning power. In 2004, the estimated lifetime earnings for workers, based on the completed level of education were as follows: non-high school graduate—$1,051,080; high school graduate—$1,429,000; some college—$1,675,880; college graduate (bachelor's degree)—$2,288.800; and, professional degree—$4,000,000. An overview of these figures shows that with a professional degree, a person will earn nearly twice as much as a college graduate, almost three times as much as a person with some college, nearly three times as much as a high school graduate, and four times as much as a person who does not graduate from high school.

We all know that this life is temporary in the light of eternity, that money isn't everything, and that we should not desire to be rich. But, if we are willing to put forth the time and effort to get an education, then we can better provide for our families and be in a position to help others and make contributions to advance the cause of God.

The idea of getting an education is not a simple decision. Studies show that the majority of college graduates end up working in a field that has nothing to do with the degree they received. A wise plan would be for a young person to take a battery of aptitude tests to determine his interest and then match them with a field of study for which there will be jobs available. Crown Ministries (www.crown.org) has a good self-administered aptitude test called *Career Direct*. Once you find an area of study that will prepare you for available jobs, then you will know that the money you spend for college—that might even include student loans—will not be wasted.

Service Industries Expected to Have the Greatest Employment Potential

- **Computer technology**
- **Health care**
- **Business services**
- **Social services**
- **Sales and retailing**
- **Hospitality and food services**
- **Management and human resources**
- **Education**
- **Financial services**

To be assured of job availability, it would be prudent to obtain an education that would fit you for one of these areas of service. You should also keep in mind your personal values and service goals.

Opportunity Cost and Money Management

When we spend money on current living expenses and entertainment, it reduces the amount that we can save and invest for the future. Obviously, the opposite is also true: saving and investing for the future reduces the amount that

we can spend now. We will address retirement and estate planning in Chapters 9 and following, but in the overall estate plan, we must consider that during the last part of our lives we will all come to the point that, because of physical or mental limitations, we will no longer be able to be gainfully employed. That being the case, we must plan ahead for that time. There must be an income stream that will provide for our needs when we can no longer work. This is why some of present earnings should be set aside for future needs. Be aware that Social Security was designed to supplement retirement income, not to provide for all retirement needs.

When we buy on credit, it ties up our future income. In like manner, when we use our savings for purchases, it results in lost interest. It means the original purpose for our savings must be delayed. There are many trade-offs that we make in making our spending decisions. For example, comparison shopping can save money, but it takes up your valuable time.

Money Management Documents

When you really get serious about proper money management, you will need to have records and documents and a safe and convenient place to store them. At a minimum you will need a balance sheet (included at the end of this lesson as Form #2) a goals sheet (also at the end of this lesson), a cash flow sheet (it outlines your current monthly income and expenses), a written budget (we use spending plan interchangeably with budget), a savings plan, and a retirement plan.

Financial records are kept to help make spending decisions, to plan for future spending, and to be able to pay bills on time. By doing a balance sheet at the beginning of each year, you can see changes in your net worth and thereby determine if your plan is working. Records also help you make good investment decisions and to easily fill out your income tax forms.

Items that you refer to often should be kept in your home file. This would include such items as personal and employment records, tax records, financial services records, money management records discussed above, credit records, and consumer purchase records and warranties in case an item or appliance becomes defective. Also kept at home are insurance and investment records and estate planning and retirement records. Costs for home improvement should be kept to determine the basis (equity) in your home for capital gains purposes when you sell. These records also help you monitor your home maintenance. Car records are important. You should know where your title(s) is(are) and keep track of maintenance.

Records that would be hard to replace should be kept in a safe deposit box. These include such things as birth, marriage, and death certificates; citizenship and military papers; adoption and custody papers; serial numbers; and, photos of valuables. You would also store here your Certificates of Deposit, mortgage papers, deeds, titles, and life insurance policies. Stock and bond certificates, coins and other collectibles, and a copy of your will and other trust documents should also be kept in your safe deposit box.

Your Guideline Budget (Spending Plan)

Your family or personal guideline budget is your day-to-day financial planning document. We have included a budget and detailed explanatory information in Chapter 5. Most families will spend everything they make and then some if they don't have a budget. We strongly encourage you to prepare a simple budget and use it to guide your financial decisions.

Debt is Bad

In a recent year credit card issuers in the United States stuffed mailboxes with more than 7 billion offers. Debt is now the most highly advertised commodity in Western society! As you would expect, people, businesses, and even governments are accepting the offers of credit and are sinking deeper and deeper into debt-bondage.

Personal bankruptcies are at an all-time high with more than 30,000 U. S. families filing for bankruptcy protection every week! Giant corporations are imploding and taking down with them the pension funds of many of their long-time employees. And over the last 30 years, the United States has been transformed by its balance of payments deficits from the world's largest creditor into the world's most heavily indebted nation.

The housing market, one of the major factors in the U. S. economy, has become a serious concern. The sub-prime mortgage implosion and the record number of foreclosures have dramatically changed the housing and real estate industry. High fuel prices have changed much in the auto industry as well as the driving and spending habits of consumers. The *Wall Street Journal*'s money magazine, *Smart Money*, reported that *"The average household is keeping track of 14 credit cards, which helps explain why Americans incur almost $1.4 billion a month in late fees"* (September 2008).

Strange and unusual things are happening in the world of credit, debt, and finance. During the second half of the 1990s, dot. coms and telcos burned through cash as if there was no tomorrow. As it turned out, for many of them there wasn't. The extraordinary economic growth and stock market boom during this period gave rise to the belief that a "new paradigm" had made the business cycle obsolete. Almost overnight, it became obvious that corporate America had made tremendous mistakes during the bubble era. In 2002, the public learned that many of the country's largest corporations had resorted to fraud in an attempt to cover them up. Scandal followed scandal. In quick succession Enron Corporation, Global Crossing, and WorldCom filed for bankruptcy. Then when Arthur Andersen, one of the "Big Five" accounting firms, disintegrated after it was found guilty of obstructing justice by destroying documents in order to cover up malpractices at Enron, faith in the entire system was shaken to the core.

Many lessons should have been learned from that economic mess. For example, families should not assume that their bank or their credit card company has their best interest at heart and will properly guide and protect them. (Corporate greed has totally neutralized courtesy and personal concern in the banking business.) Families must look out for themselves. They should not get in debt over their heads. They should only make credit decisions based on their budget and reasonable capabilities.

Astonishingly, in spite of everything that was going wrong, consumers were still spending as though nothing was wrong. Many were buying expensive homes with "interest only" loans. Their creditors encouraged them! Borrowing had never been easier or cheaper. Mortgage financing and consumer credit were flowing freely. During the spending spree, one bank chairman stated, "You'd have to be an insolvent arsonist not to get a loan right now."

This was only the beginning. Financial problems affecting families continued. In 2008 the sub-prime mortgage meltdown caused many Fortune 500 investment banks to fail like falling dominoes. To save the credit market, Congress bailed out AIG to the tune of $85 billion and authorized an unprecedented $700 billion to prop up the failing credit banking system. Nervous investors in the fear and greed cycle of Wall Street dumped stocks that caused an overall drop in the Dow Jones' of over 30%!

But the big question is: "How much more debt can the typical consumer handle?" Almost every indicator suggests that consumers are over-indebted relative to their income and earnings prospects. In 2006 Americans saved at the unreal rate of -1% (that's minus 1%)! That means that consumers spent more than they earned and even used some of their savings in the process. Debt cannot continue to expand more rapidly than income indefinitely—at either the household level or at the national level.

Which Way for the Christian?

As Bible-believing Christians we live in this scary world we've just described. How are we to relate to all of this? Do we just go along with the flow? Or should our lives and financial management reflect a different paradigm?

The answer is, of course, axiomatic. We see the world through different eyes. We have been told, *"Do not love the world or the things in the world. If anyone loves the world, the love of the Father is not in him. For all that is in the world—the lust of the flesh, the lust of the eyes, and the pride of life—is not of the Father but is of the world. And the world is passing away, and the lust of it; but he who does the will of God abides forever"* (1 John 2:15-17). We have direct inside information that the world as we know it will end soon at the Second Coming of Jesus and that everything earthly will then be burned up. That will reduce its value considerably! *"But the day of the Lord will come as a thief in the night, in which the heavens will pass away with a great noise, and the elements will melt with fervent heat; both the earth and the works that are in it will be burned up"* (2 Peter 3:10).

Jesus said that we are to be a light to the world (Matthew 5:14) and as salt that gives flavor to life (vs. 13). Unfortunately however, in the management of money, the world is often salting us more than we are salting it. Many Christians find themselves mired in debt just like the people of the world.

Reasons for Financial Problems

Over many years of financial counseling and teaching Biblical stewardship, we have found three primary reasons that people get into financial difficulty. We will list them here in the order of greatest frequency.

The first is ignorance. Many people, even college graduates, are financially illiterate. They were simply never exposed to the Biblical or even secular principles of money management. There is hope for these people! This book will provide a simple outline of these principles and how to apply them.

The second reason for financial difficulties is greed—selfishness. In response to advertising and personal wants, people simply live beyond their means. They are not willing to live in, drive, or wear what they can really afford. Many of these same people also feel that they are just too poor to tithe. As a consequence, they live their lives without God's promised wisdom and blessing. (See Proverbs 3:5-10). There is hope for these people also, but it requires a change of heart—and the reception of a gift from God called contentment. Paul exhorts, *"Now godliness with contentment is great gain. For we brought nothing into this world, and it is certain we can carry nothing out. And having food and clothing, with these we shall be content. But those who desire to be rich fall into temptation and a snare, and into many foolish and harmful lusts which drown men in destruction and perdition"* (1 Timothy 6:6-9).

The third reason people find themselves in financial difficulty is because of an unfortunate tragedy. They may have experienced a serious illness without adequate health insurance. They may have been abandoned by a spendthrift marriage partner. A natural disaster may have wiped out their possessions. Or, they may have been born and raised in abject poverty. There is hope for these people, too. Though their path is more difficult, it can be overcome. Change may come in the support of Christian friends; the counsel and/or assistance of godly counselors; hard work coupled with a good education; and the blessing and providence of God.

Seven Biblical Principles

The writing team has discovered seven Biblical principles that give practical guidance about what to do to achieve peace and freedom in your financial world. Look up these texts and mark them in your Bible.

God is the owner of everything. (Psalms 24:1; 50:12; 1 Chronicles 29:13, 14) As Christians we understand that we brought nothing into this world and that we are taking nothing out. While we live on this earth, we are simply managers of what God has entrusted to us. Faithfulness is all that matters.

God and His wisdom and counsel must have first place in your life. (Proverbs 3:5-9; Matthew 6:33) God can see our lives from the beginning to the end. He knows what is best for us and desires that we prosper. This means more than the simplistic question, "What Would Jesus Do?" We ask instead, "What is His counsel in this area of my life?"

Your purpose in life is to glorify God. (Matthew 5:16; 1 Corinthians 10:31) The worldling seeks prosperity in order to spend and accumulate. The Christian seeks to prosper in order to provide for personal needs, the needs of others, and to help advance the cause of God. The Christian is God's ambassador.

Prosperity is having what you need when you need it. (Philippians 4:19; Matthew 28:20; Isaiah 26:3) God has not promised us that if we become Christians, we will become wealthy by the world's standards. But He has promised that if we serve Him, He will provide for our needs, be with us wherever we go, and give us peace in our hearts.

Debt is bad. (Proverbs 22:7; Deuteronomy 28:15-68; Romans 13:8; Psalms 37:21) If you recognize and follow this single principle, it would do more than anything else to bring peace to our families and prosperity to the cause of God. Debt causes strife in families and stress in individual lives.

The tithe is the minimum testimony of our Christian commitment. (Genesis 14:20; 28:20-22; Leviticus 27:30; Malachi 3:6-11) From the perspective of those who read through the Bible each year to review the big picture, we can tell you that nowhere in the Bible does God suggest that less than a tenth is His. Failure to recognize and practice this principle cuts us off from God's wisdom and blessing. (See Deuteronomy 28:15-68.)

Everyone must give an account to God of his money management. (Matthew 25:19; 2 Corinthians 5:10; Revelation 22:12.) There is nothing more certain in Scripture than the fact that we must all face the judgment bar of God. When settling accounts with those who are faithful God says, *"Well done, good and faithful servant; you were faithful over a few things, I will make you ruler over many things. Enter into the joy of your lord"* (Matthew 25:21).

Help the Poor—Store Up Treasure in Heaven

It should be more than obvious to all who study Christian stewardship and money management that God does not need "our money," and that He could easily take care of all the poor Himself. Yet He allows us to aid the poor in order to assist in the transformation of our characters and to see in the depths of poverty the result of sin in the world. But, characteristically, God has several blessings in mind for us. In addition to the two mentioned above, God also promises to add to our heavenly treasure when we help the poor. When we help the poor, we are not really giving our money away—we are storing it up in heaven.

All three of the synoptic gospels tell the story of the Rich Young Ruler. (See Matthew 19:16-26, Mark 10:17-27, and Luke 18:18-27) In each account Jesus told the young man that if he would give to the poor, he would have treasure in heaven. It is also interesting to note in Matthew 25:31-46 in the account of the great final judgment that the line is drawn between the saved and the lost by what they did for Jesus in the person of the poor and the suffering. *"Then the King will say to those on His right hand, 'Come, you blessed of My Father, inherit the kingdom prepared for you from the foundation of the world: for I was hungry and you gave Me food; I was thirsty and you gave Me drink; I was a stranger and you took Me in; I was naked and you clothed Me; I was sick and your visited Me; I was in prison and you came to Me...inasmuch as you did it to one of the least of these My brethren, you did it to Me."*

It should be obvious from these passages that it is important to Jesus that we make room to assist the poor in our financial planning. Perhaps Zacchaeus was smarter than we give him credit for. After a single encounter with Jesus, instead of going away sorrowfully as did the rich young ruler, he announced that he was giving half of his goods to the poor. Responding to the tax collector's transformation, Jesus proclaimed, *"Today salvation has come to this house"* (Luke 19:9). Wouldn't you like Jesus to say that at your house?

In Chapter 1 we reviewed the baseline of Biblical money management—accepting the Lordship of Christ. In Chapter 2 we have looked at the base line of money management—the balance sheet and the basic stewardship principles. To prepare for your next group meeting, complete the following assignments.

Assignment for this lesson:

1. Memorize Proverbs 3:9, 10.
2. Pray for the members of your study group by name.
3. Complete the balance sheet—Form #2.
4. Put your financial goals down on paper using Form #3.

Planning for the Cycle of Life

Memory Verse: (Proverbs 3:9,10)

Honor the Lord with your possessions, and with the firstfruits of all your increase, so your barns will be filled plenty and your vats will overflow with new wine."

PRAYER TIME:

Make a list of those in your group who have asked for special prayer needs this week and pray for them each day.

_____

_____

Pray also for God's wisdom and blessing as you develop your financial plan.

Introduction:

An old adage says, "There is nothing certain but death and taxes." Of course, as Christians, we must add the certainty of our salvation and the fact that we must all face the judgment bar of God. We must all give an account of our stewardship. *"After a long time the lord of those servants came and settled accounts with them"* (Matthew 25:19).

We look with hope to the second coming of Christ. But even though we know from the signs Jesus gave us that the coming is near, He also tells us to *"occupy till I come"* (Luke 19:13). The NKJV says, *"Do business till I come."* So unless Jesus returns before we die, we will have the cycle of life to plan, live out, and defend in the judgment.

This cycle can be divided into four sections of about 20 years each. We call this the cycle of life, but it is only cyclical because it is the fate of all mankind. But for us individually it is really a line that stretches from birth to death. The segments of life are the learning years, the earning years, the conserving years, and the returning years. Some secular financial planners divide the life cycle, time line, or estate plan into three segments: accumulation, conservation, and distribution.

As Bible-believers we have good solid counsel that can apply to each of these segments of life. By following the counsel we can have the abundant life that Jesus came to provide. (See John 10:10).

STUDY TIME:

Day One:

Read chapter 2 and begin memorizing the memory text.

Day Two:

Spend more time on the memory text.

Begin to fill in the balance sheet on the next page. Concentrate specifically today on the assets that are in your possession or control. Try to be realistic in your valuations of things. You might need to seek assistance on the value of certain items. This section would also include coin and stamp collections and other such items.

Day Three:

Begin to say the memory text without looking at the words.

Finish the balance sheet by listing all of the debts you owe. Be sure to include all of your debts such as student loans, family loans, time share properties, etc.

Day Four:

Begin working on your list of short-term and long-term goals. The short-term goals are those that you can accomplish in 1-2 years. Long-term goals are those that may require more than 2 years.

Short-term goals would include: being systematic in tithe and offerings, paying off credit card balances, completing a balance sheet, establishing a budget, living within your income, starting a savings plan from a payroll deduction, etc.

Long-term goals would include pre-paying (before they run their full term) larger debts such as student loans, automobiles, your home mortgage, etc. It would also include saving up to pay cash for your next car and funding a retirement supplemental plan.

Day Five:

Fill out the balance of the Financial Goals form. This time state your goals in measurable terms. Make the goals specific here. Set a time frame for accomplishing your goals both short-term and long-term. Put the start and end dates in your planner or calendar. For example, you may say, "I will pay off my Visa card balance by _____." Write down what action you will take to accomplish your goals.

Day Six:

Review your balance sheet and goals work-sheet and see if there are other items that should be included on either form. Begin to implement the goals.

Personal/Family Balance Sheet

The purpose of the balance sheet is to determine your current financial position as of a particular day. So the first line to fill out is the date.

Instructions: List the current values of each item in the asset categories below. List the amounts owed for the various liabilities. Subtract the total liabilities from total assets to determine your net worth.

Balance Sheet as of (today's date) _____

ASSETS: (things you own)

Liquid assets:

Checking account balance   _____

Savings/money market accounts   _____

Cash value of life insurance   _____

Other_____   _____

Total liquid assets   _____

Household assets and possessions:

Current market value of home   _____

Other real estate   _____

Current value of automobile(s)   _____

Recreational vehicle(s)   _____

Personal property; furniture, tools, etc.   _____

Stereo, camera(s), computer(s)   _____

Other_____   _____

Total household assets   _____

Investment assets:

Saving certificates   _____

Stocks and bonds   _____

Individual retirement accounts   _____

Mutual funds   _____

Other_____   _____

Total investment assets   _____

Total Assets: _____

LIABILITIES: (debt you owe)

Current liabilities:

Charge accounts and credit card balances   _____

Auto loans   _____

Other monthly payments (not utilities)   _____

Other_____   _____

Total current liabilities   _____

Long-term liabilities:

Home mortgage   _____

Student loans   _____

Other_____   _____

Total long-term liabilities   _____

Total Liabilities   _____

NET WORTH (assets minus liabilities)   _____

Creating Financial Goals

Based on your current situation as demonstrated in your personal/family balance sheet or expectations for the future, create your financial goals, short-term and long-term using the following guidelines.

Step 1. Create realistic and specific goals based on your life situation.

A. SHORT-TERM GOALS _____

_____

_____

B. LONG-TERM GOALS _____

_____

_____

Step 2. State your goals in specific, measurable terms.

a. _____

b. _____

_____

Step 3. Describe the time frame for accomplishing your goals.

a. _____

b. _____

_____

Step 4. Indicate an action to be taken to achieve your goals.

a. _____

b. _____

_____

If you don't know where you are going, any road will take you there. But as a Bible-believing Christian—you know! God has a plan for your life and that includes being a faithful steward of the resources that He has entrusted to you. So make a plan and follow the plan. You will get to where you want to go and with much less stress.

Order my steps in thy word: and let not any iniquity have dominion over me.
Psalms 119:133

Lesson 3

Looking at Giving

Memory Text: Deuteronomy 16:16, 17

"They shall not appear before the Lord empty-handed. Every man shall give as he is able, according to the blessing of the Lord your God which He has given you."

As we noted from the memory texts of the first two lessons, when it comes to money management we are told to put God first. Both Old and New Testaments contain this injunction. In this lesson we will review the Biblical counsel regarding tithes and offerings. We have never encountered a family who, looking back on its lives has stated, "We wish we hadn't spent all that money on tithes and offerings." Most faithful Christian families spontaneously respond that they are confident that God has blessed and provided for their family and actually can point to specific instances where they know God intervened on their behalf.

Giving to God, being financially faithful is not just a spiritual commitment or a philosophical choice. It is by far the most significant financial factor for life management. God says, if you put Me first, I will give you wisdom and bless you. For confirmation of this, read Proverbs 3:5-10, Deuteronomy 28:1-14, and Malachi 3:6-12. We put God first and receive His special blessings when we acknowledge that God created everything (Genesis 1:1) and therefore owns everything (Psalms 24:1). We understand that He sustains us and we, in turn, manage what He has given us by

first returning His part, the tithe (Leviticus 27:30), and then bringing offerings proportionate to our income and His blessings. Believe it or not, this is the foundational principle for Biblical money management!

When you read the writings of non-Christian financial counselors, they almost all contain the counsel, "Pay yourself first." What they mean by this is that your own situation should be your first consideration. But this plan puts God in second place at best and violates His direct commands. The Bible says, *"Blessed is the man who walks not in the counsel of the ungodly, nor stands in the path of sinners, nor sits in the seat of the scornful; but his delight is in the law of the Lord, and in His law he meditates day and night. He shall be like a tree planted by the rivers of water, that brings forth its fruit in its season, whose leaf also shall not wither; and whatever he does shall prosper"* (Psalms 1:1-3).

Why Do We Give?

"I hate writing out a tithe check. But I will tithe even if it kills me," one woman insisted. What drove her to this attitude? Why did she continue to give even though she really did not want to do so? Giving and offerings mean different things to different people. People have different reasons why they put money in an envelope and call it tithe or offering. Similarly, and unfortunately, even church leaders have used different ways to motivate people to give. Frequently traditional, human motivations are used. For example, we use recognition and praise when we fundraise. Sometimes we use guilt. At other times, we emphasize what giving will do for the donor. All these methods focus on the donors and their needs or desires. All these methods strengthen the power of selfishness.

First, we must remember that giving—for a Christian—is an act of worship. The primary purpose for tithes and offerings is to give glory to God, to recognize Him as Creator, and to integrate Him into the material side of life. Appeals to traditional human motivations may actually reinforce chains of selfishness and sin. Thus, we must ask ourselves the following questions: What can you really give to God? Can we as Christians give anything more than our own hearts? What makes our tithe and offerings worship?

As Bible-believing Christians, we do not give because we have too much. We give in response to experienced grace and in thanksgiving for God's blessings. We give to the things we believe will advance the cause of God. And for our estate planning we conclude that since God is the rightful Owner of everything, when we are finished with the resources that He has entrusted to us, we return them to God by helping others or making contributions to advance His cause.

Truly, all we have and are belong to God. Tithe is worship when we recognize our relationship with God. Offerings are worship when, in partnership with Him, we invest God's money in His kingdom. They become an extension of our partnership with God. Without this partnership, we cannot worship Him with offerings—they are only payoffs. Offerings reflect our hearts and our experience with God and are the result of the Holy Spirit's guidance in intimate partnership. In our present day economy, tithe is returned and offerings are given in the form of money or

its equivalents, such as checks or other financial transactions. In this lesson we will discuss tithe and offerings from their Biblical perspective and then make a current practical application.

Biblical Tithing

When we speak of tithing, it is not a matter of generosity or gratitude. It is a matter of simple honesty—honesty with God. The Bible states that the tithe is holy and belongs to God. *"All the tithe of the land…is the Lord's. It is holy to the Lord"* (Leviticus 27:30). The very first thing the Bible establishes about God is that He is the Creator of heaven and earth (Genesis 1:1), and this forms the foundation for everything else the Bible says about Him, about who we are, and about how we should relate to Him. In fact, the phrase "heaven and earth," used so frequently in the Old Testament, indicates totality and is, in a sense, the Hebrew way of expressing what the Greeks communicated through the term kosmos, the totality of the ordered universe.

Since God is the Creator of heaven and earth, He is also the exclusive and rightful Owner of everything. He is the Creator/Owner. We are the creature/steward.

So what exactly is tithe? The tithe is a tenth part of our income or our increase, if we are self-employed. We understand that this is the part of our God-given increase that He claims as His own. We know that tithe means tenth because in both the Old and New Testaments the words for tithe and tenth are used interchangeably. For example, the first mention of tithe in the Bible is Genesis 14:20. Abram gave Melchizedek, the priest of the most High God, *"a tithe of all"* the spoils of Sodom which were given to him by the king of Sodom. It is interesting that the last mention of tithe in the Bible is in Hebrews 7:1-10. This is the New Testament recounting of the story of Abraham [by this time his name had been changed] and his encounter with Melchizedek. In this account we are told, *"The patriarch Abraham gave a tenth of the spoils."* (vs. 4).

A further point that we must observe from this experience is that the tithe was not just a

Jewish ordinance with the Levitical priesthood. In this story, Melchizedek was God's priest who received tithe before there ever was a tribe of Levi, and the final mention of tithe in Hebrews 7 mentions *"our Lord [who] arose from Judah . . . and is a priest forever according to the order of Melchizedek."* (vss. 14-17).

The Central Storehouse

So far we see that the tithe is a tenth of our income or increase. It is holy and belongs to God. So now, what should be done with it? Here again the Bible is very clear and specific. We are told that we should *"Bring all the tithes [the whole tithe] into the storehouse, that there may be food in My house"* (Malachi 3:10). This begs the question, "What and where is the storehouse? By studying the Bible we see that God's people in Old Testament times had no problem identifying the storehouse. They all went there three times a year!

Just before he died Moses gathered all Israel together and gave them three sermons or public presentations. They are recorded for us in the Bible as the book of Deuteronomy. He stated that even though they were to be settled in and scattered all over Canaan, three times a year, they were to assemble at the Lord's house for praise, worship and the delivery of their tithes and offerings.

"But [when] ye go over Jordan, and dwell in the land which the LORD your God giveth you to inherit, and [when] he giveth you rest from all your enemies round about, so that ye dwell in safety; then there shall be a place which the LORD your God shall choose to cause his name to dwell there; thither shall ye bring all that I command you; your burnt offerings, and your sacrifices, your tithes, and the heave offering of your hand, and all your choice vows which ye vow unto the LORD" (Deut. 12:10,11).

Three Times a Year

Three times each year all the males in Israel were to appear before the Lord: at Passover,

Pentecost, and the Feast of Tabernacles. *"Three times in a year shall all thy males appear before the LORD thy God in the place which he shall choose; in the feast of unleavened bread, and in the feast of weeks, and in the feast of tabernacles: and they shall not appear before the LORD empty-handed. Every man [shall give] as he is able, according to the blessing of the LORD thy God which he hath given thee"* (Deut. 16:16, 17). (See also Exodus 23:14-17.)

"Anciently the Lord instructed His people to assemble three times a year for His worship. To these holy convocations the children of Israel came, bringing to the house of God their tithes, their sin offerings, and their offerings of gratitude. They met to recount God's mercies, to make known His wonderful works, and to offer praise and thanksgiving to His name. And they were to unite in the sacrificial service which pointed to Christ as the Lamb of God that taketh away the sin of the world. Thus they were to be preserved from the corrupting power of worldliness and idolatry. Faith and love and gratitude were to be kept alive in their hearts, and through their association together in this sacred service they were to be bound closer to God and to one another" (Testimonies for the Church, vol. 6, p. 39, underlining by editor).

Here is the bottom line: The Israelites gave at least one-fourth of their income to God in the form of tithes, thank offerings, support of the temple, and gifts to the poor. In addition, most of these donations were personally delivered by each family, in kind or in cash equivalents, to the central storehouse, at first to Shiloh and then to Jerusalem. This personal delivery system required them to be away from home and work at least one month each year. **Yet the 25% giving and the one month away from home were actually the basis for their prosperity and blessing—and they knew it!**

David promised, *"I will pay my vows to the Lord now in the presence of all His people, in the courts of the Lord's house, in the midst of you, O Jerusalem"* (Ps. 116:18,19). This was the practice of all the faithful in Israel. (See also Ps. 122:1-4.)

The Use of the Tithe

Again the Bible is very clear and specific about the use of the tithe. God explicitly stated in Numbers 18:21, *"Behold, I have given the children of Levi all the tithes in Israel as an inheritance in return for the work which they perform, the work of the tabernacle of meeting."* It is clear that the tithe belongs to God and He could, in fact, do whatever He wanted to with it. It is also clear that His chosen purpose for the tithe is to support religious leaders and their families. Accordingly, in harmony with this Bible principle, the Seventh-day Adventist Church organization has designated the local conference as the storehouse to which the tithe should be returned and from which the gospel ministry would receive their salaries. In addition, the local conference gives support to the furtherance of the gospel into all the world. For the convenience of the church members and as part of their worship experience, the tithe is returned through the local church where membership is held, and the local treasurer forwards all the tithe to the conference storehouse from which the religious workers are paid. This system, outlined by God, has enabled His church to have a global and ever growing impact in the world.

What About Offerings?

Our offerings come from the 90% that remains in our possession after our tithe is returned to God. This is where generosity begins. There are several different types of offerings given by God's people that are recorded in the Bible. There were sin offerings—given as a response to experienced grace; thank offerings—given to recognize God's protection, blessings of health, prosperity, and sustaining power; offerings for the poor; and, offerings to build and maintain the house of worship. With the possible exception of the temple tax, offerings were not given according to a percentage as was the tithe. In many cases the offerings would exceed the tithe, when one's heart was touched in response to calls to build

the tabernacle, etc. God's simple command was, *"Every man shall give as he is able, according to the blessing of the Lord your God which He has given you"* (Deuteronomy 16:17). We may designate our offerings to specific purposes today such as local church needs, the work of our conference, and the needs of the world church, but they are still based on our thankfulness for God's blessings to us.

Failure to bring offerings, in addition to the tithe, to the storehouse was considered by God to be robbery of Him. Obviously that is where the sin offerings and the temple support offerings would go. Unlike the tithe, some of our offerings can be discretionary. In other words, we can designate a portion to help the poor, the orphans and widows and to give support to projects we believe are supporting the work of God on earth.

Motivation in Giving

Our first challenge is to grow spiritually so that our giving is an extension of our faith walk with God. Giving without a faith relationship cannot be worship. Giving based on something other than the faith relationship and the assurance of salvation becomes false worship.

The best giving follows vision, not duty. This vision must have a Biblical origin. We do not have to wonder about God's vision. We can go to Scripture to discover it and then articulate it in the contemporary context. We find this vision in proportion to God's ability and His ability to be involved with what His Church is doing. A Biblical vision for ministry and the church provides a powerful foundation for seeing what God is doing.

The best giving follows mission, not structure. We understand that structure and organization are necessary to realistically take on our commission as Christians. Matthew 28:18-20 provides the clearest and most powerful mission a church could find. God promises to be with us always, even unto the end of the world. This assures us that in joining this mission, we walk with God in intimate partnership.

The best giving follows people, not programs. God is, first of all, a personal God, and we need a personal touch when working for Him. Thus, we need to be personally involved and not just giving as a substitute for that involvement.

The best giving follows passion, not pressure. This means that our hearts have to be involved, and we must have a personal commitment. Christianity is about a passionate involvement with the Lord of the universe. True giving by a Christian comes as a result of a personal commitment to and heart involvement with this incredible God. The Bible calls this type of giving willing gifts (Exodus 35:5) and cheerful gifts (2 Corinthians 9:7).

The best giving follows growth and progress, not maintenance. The ground we have conquered for Christ must be maintained, but significant portions of our time and resources should be used to continue to advance the work of God in the earth.

The best giving follows information, not promotion. Only the Holy Spirit has the right to convict people regarding their giving. We can help the Holy Spirit by providing information. That information must be complete, transparent, and understandable. In today's world, what is unknown, misunderstood, or hidden is automatically suspect. Accurate information of what God is doing and how we can join with Him in His mission helps us in our giving.

The best giving follows conviction, not manipulation. Only the Holy Spirit can bring about conviction. Only God can create the desire, and when He does, He gives the power and the desire to follow through on that conviction.

Let's remember that God is the Owner-Partner. We are managing partners. Everything belongs to God, and we manage His investments in partnership with Him. We acknowledge that relationship through the tithe we return to Him, and we invest directly in His kingdom. We manage His assets, and we invest them in His kingdom through offerings and in the way we care for our families.

Jesus clearly portrays money as a direct competition to God and speaks of the impossibility of serving both money and God (Matthew 6:24). Tithe is one of the primary tools God uses to establish Himself as Lord in our lives. How we deal with money, and more specifically, how we deal with tithe, is a reflection of where God is in our lives.

When our hearts are right, we worship God each time we return our tithe and offerings to Him. Tithing is a worship experience that accepts our relationship with God. It is a worship experience where we acknowledge God as Creator and accept His ownership of who we are and what we have. Claiming ownership for ourselves usurps God's right and His position. Tithing reminds us that redemption restores God's ownership in our lives. *"You are to be holy to me because I, the Lord, am holy, and I have set you apart from the nations to be my own"* (Leviticus 20:26).

When we tithe, we consciously profess our trust in God to care and provide for us. When we tithe, we confess who He is in our lives and recognize His guidance and love. When we tithe, we deliberately choose to rely on Him. Thus, we follow His guidance to not worry, and *"seek first His kingdom and His righteousness"* (Matthew 6:33). Only when we experience salvation can we worship God. Only when we surrender to His lordship can we truly tithe.

Understanding tithe in this way leads us to realize that tithe is holy, unique, and different. It belongs to the Holy One; it is His to administer. Part of our worship with tithe is turning it over to Him to manage. What happens to the tithe is not our responsibility; our only responsibility is to worship God. However, when, as a part of church leadership, we manage tithe funds for God's church, we must always remember that what we manage belongs to God, not to us.

A worship lifestyle includes accepting the responsibility to administer all of God's gifts in partnership with Him. Returning tithe is not a way of paying God off with 10% blackmail, so we then can do what we want with the remaining 90%. Neither is tithe a tip to God, thanking Him for what we have received. Tithe is a sign of our willingness to manage what belongs to God—in all of life—in an intimate walk with Him.

For tithing to be truly worship, we need to ask ourselves some questions on a regular basis:

Who owns the home we live in? Who owns all the property we manage? Who has given us talent and strength to earn a living? Who has priority in our choices for everyday life? On Whom do we rely each day? Do we really allow God to be God in every area of life?

So, how do we make our returning of the tithe truly worship? The answer lies in our attitude and action. Tithing as worship starts with a personal acceptance of Jesus Christ as Savior and Lord. Next is a decision to consciously recognize God as the Owner of all that we have and are. Then comes an attitude of management on our part rather than ownership.

Now, turn that attitude into acts of conscious worship and make tithing an intentional act, not just a habit: Fill out your tithe envelope with a prayer of thanksgiving and praise; place the envelope in the offering plate with the assurance of divine partnership; live every moment acknowledging Jesus as Lord of your life; and, do every deed conscious of the divine partnership you have with God.

As we continue to explore the Biblical record, we find tithing connected with the call to revival (2 Chronicles 31, Nehemiah 12-13, and Malachi 3). The real issue is always worship—how we acknowledge our relationship with God as Owner and Redeemer.

One of the most important points for understanding God's rationale for tithing is found in what Jesus said in Matthew 6:25-34. He placed money and material things in direct competition with God in our lives. He confronts us with a choice as to Whom we will serve and how we will serve Him. It is interesting to note that the context is the basic necessities of life, not luxuries. A life focused on providing the bare necessities of food and clothing is identified as pagan. Instead of such a focus, Jesus challenges us: *"But seek first the kingdom of God and His righteousness, and all these things shall be added to you"* (v. 33).

Though it does not appear in the immediate context of Matthew 6, tithing is one of God's primary tools in our "discipleship journey" to help us keep our focus on Him while we deal with the material world. As we tithe, we place God first. We acknowledge Him as the Owner of everything we have in our hands. We admit we are stewards—managers.

Simple Steps for Joyful Tithing

Step 1: Accept our relationship with God

First we must recognize that true worship can come only from a heart in tune with God. So, the first step is to accept our relationship with God. This starts with confessing our sin, accepting forgiveness, and rejoicing in our eternal life. We are then in a new relationship with Jesus, so when we return our tithe, we are recognizing our salvation in Christ and celebrating Him as our Redeemer. This redemption re-establishes His ownership of our lives.

Step 2: Accept God as Creator

The second step to make returning our tithe worship is to accept God as our Creator. As such, He can also re-create and give us new life. As Creator, He provides for all our needs. We acknowledge this as worshipping Him by putting Him first in returning our tithe. By seeking His kingdom and His righteousness first, we make a choice to live a new life. In this way, tithing is a tool that helps us change our priorities.

Step 3: Surrender our ownership and accept His

Tithing is worship when it comes from one who has accepted the reality of God as Owner. This is the next step. We choose to surrender our ownership and accept His. It means we recognize that everything we have in our hands belongs to God. We are only managing it. We worship God with our tithe to remind us that everything belongs to Him, and we need His help to manage the 100% for His honor and glory. In this way we accept our responsibility to carefully oversee all the gifts He has placed in our care.

Step 4: Recognize God's care, guidance, and love

Also we make returning our tithe an act of worship when we recognize God's providential care, guidance, and love to us. The tithe we return to God reminds us that He cares for us; that He is intimately involved in all the details of our lives; and, that before we tithe, He has already provided for all our daily needs. We present our tithe to Him with grateful hearts, recognizing the bountiful blessings He has given us, because we can give tithe only if we have already received His blessings.

Step 5: Accept that we are to be holy to God

Tithing as worship also provides an opportunity for us to accept that we are "to be holy to" God (Lev. 20:26). Because He is Owner and we belong to Him, we are holy—set apart for His special use. In tithing we can recognize that we are completely His and every part of our lives belongs to Him. Thus our tithe becomes a confession that we, too, are "set apart" for God.

Step 6: Re-consecrate our lives to God

When we accept tithe as holy, that it belongs to God, we recognize the blessing that is ours in handling that which is holy. To do this well, we must bring our tithe to Him in the context of our daily walk with God. Tithing then becomes an opportunity for complete re-consecration of our lives to God. We can rejoice in the reality of our salvation and acceptance in Christ. We can accept our new life in Him. We can celebrate God's goodness in caring for us in the material world and thus recognize that He has also cared for us in the spiritual world. Tithe then becomes a testimony to God and our own hearts that we accept and worship God in our daily living as disciples.

A thirteen-year-old boy on one of the South Pacific Islands demonstrated this attitude of worship. Bringing a large fish he had caught, he told the local elder of his church that this was his tithe and asked how he should deal with it. The elder explained what he should do with the "tithe fish" and congratulated the boy on his good catch of ten fish. The young man replied, "Oh no! This is the first one. The others are still in the ocean. I'm going after them now."

Truly, tithing provides us a tool to worship God, placing Him first in our lives in every way, because tithing is tangible recognition of our incredible relationship with Him.

God Provides the Offerings

Now, let's look at offerings. We know the story well, but do we understand it? God spoke to Abraham, telling him to go to a mountain and there offer his son as a burnt offering. Abraham obeyed and began a journey of faith that would end with an offering of praise. When Isaac asked about the offering, Abraham responded that God would provide. When they reached the top of the mountain, Abraham explained God's command.

This incredible story triggers a number of questions. How could God ask this of Abraham? How could Abraham agree? How could Isaac submit? What would we do if placed in a similar position?

The book of Hebrews helps us understand Abraham's response. *"Concluding that God was able to raise* him up, *even from the dead, from which he also received him in a figurative sense"* (Heb.11:19). And somehow, Abraham's faith was contagious. Isaac also trusted God enough to place himself on the altar.

We know the rest of the story. God provided the offering in the form of a ram caught in a thicket (Gen. 22:13). This account points to the reality that God always provides the offering, whether it is a ram on the top of a mountain or a Savior on a hill called Calvary. God always provides.

In fact, if we stop to think about it, God even provides when we give our offerings to Him. All that we have comes from His hand and belongs to Him. So, when we offer Him something, we only can give back to Him what we received from Him in the first place. What gives the offering any meaning? Our attitude!

Remember the story of Cain and Abel? Each brought an offering, but God only accepted the offering from an obedient heart.

"God does not receive the offerings of any because He needs them and cannot have glory and riches without them, but because it is best for His servants to render to God the things which are His. The freewill offerings of the humble, contrite heart He will receive and will reward the giver with the richest blessings. He receives them as the sacrifice of grateful obedience. He requires and accepts our gold and silver as an evidence that all we have and are belongs to Him. He claims and accepts the improvement of our time and of our talents as the fruit of His love existing in our hearts. To obey is better than sacrifice. Without pure love, the most expensive offering is too poor for God to accept" (*Testimonies for the Church*, vol 2, pp 652-653).

Offerings are meaningful only when they reflect who we are in relationship to God. They express our worship and praise to God and our willingness to admit that He is the Owner—that all we have comes from Him. The Psalmist challenges us: *"Ascribe to the Lord the glory due his name; bring an offering and come into his courts. Worship the Lord in the splendor of his holiness; tremble before him, all the earth"* (Psalms 96:8-9).

God has a contemporary test in the material world: offerings in possessions—regular, systematic partnership, and advanced partnership with specific conviction. The tithe comes first, and God says it is His. The returning of the tithe is a test of our loyalty. The offerings come next as a test of attitude. It is a way to provide for regular, systematic support as part of our worship to God. Then come special projects.

When it comes to offerings, God demands the best. He asks that we give Him what is most precious to us, for anything less would be a form of idolatry. For our own good, He must reside first in our hearts and lives. He calls us to give ourselves to Him in a lifestyle of worship (Rom. 12:1). Only after we have given ourselves to Him can we truly worship Him with an offering.

What about the times we casually place an offering in the plate. Is it worship? Have we given ourselves, or are we just following a habit begun in childhood? Have we reached the place of trusting God with all that is precious to us? Have we recognized that He is the Owner and that all we have comes as a blessing from His hand?

As we quietly reflect on these questions, we are compelled to confess that far too often our giving is mechanical and without thought. Often it is based on the perceived need and not as a response to God's blessings. Sometimes, it even is given grudgingly, from a sense of duty. God has a better way: *"What shall I render to the Lord for all His benefits toward me? I will take up the cup of salvation, and call upon the name of the Lord. I will pay my vows to the Lord now in the presence of all His people"* (Psalms 116:12-14).

Offerings as Worship and Praise

What then can we do to make our offerings truly an act of praise and worship? Here are a few thoughts for consideration:

- We can keep our walk with God fresh and intimate. We can spend time with Him and daily remember He has saved us through His grace.
- We can reflect on what God gave for us, all that was most precious to Him—His Son! As one man has said, "When Jesus died on Calvary, God's pockets were emptied."
- We can reflect on the reality that all we have comes from and belongs to God. He asks us to give only after we recognize that He has provided everything.
- We can thank Him for the many blessings He brings each day and live with the awareness of His provision.
- We can seek to daily praise God and joyfully acknowledge who we are in light of who He is as Creator and Redeemer.
- We can take all that is precious to us and place it in His hands, trusting Him to care for it far better than we can.
- But most of all, we can give Him our hearts, for that is all that is truly ours to surrender: *"The sacrifices of God are a broken spirit, a broken*

and a contrite heart—These, O God, You will not despise" (Psalms 51:17).

Before we can acquire the grace of giving, we must have the grace of receiving. *"Freely you have received, freely give"* (Matthew 10:8). *"God so loved the world that He gave"* (John 3:16). Only when we accept Christ do we have anything to give. The grace of giving is preceded by giving ourselves up, by making God first. We cannot give God money when He does not have our heart. We cannot buy God with our offerings. As an antidote for selfishness, offerings become an expression of gratitude. Returning tithe is recognition of who He is; offerings are an expression of gratitude. Offerings are an agent of transforming grace, because as we give, we participate in God's grace while simultaneously combating selfishness.

Offerings are a response to God's giving. They are an implementation of the partnership of God, working from God's abundance rather than humanity's scarcity. Offerings combat the selfish heart of the old sinful nature. How much should you give? Only you and God can know the answer to that question.

Here are some examples of the grace of giving: The giving for the building of the tabernacle (Ex. 36:1-6). When God's people experience redemption, they will bring until God says, "Stop!" We are tempted to say, "God doesn't have enough money, so He is going to use some of mine." Another example is Abraham giving his son as an act of obedience (Gen. 22:1-14). The widow of Zarephath (1 Kings 17:10-16) and the widow who gave her two mites (Luke 21:2-3) are other examples of grace giving. The Macedonian churches (2 Cor. 8:1-5) also exemplified the grace of giving when they gave out of their necessity and in most cases, out of their poverty, not out of their abundance.

What are God's purposes for offerings? To extend partnership with humanity; to give a testimony of praise to God; to support His mission on earth; to strengthen the unity of the Church; to provide for His church in order to help the needy.

So what is the role of the Holy Spirit in giving? To convict and guide the giver; to empower or make it possible for the giver to give; and, to guide the corporate body and its leadership in the ministry.

When we handle God's money, we are handling that which is holy. We need to maintain full integrity, full disclosure, full openness, and full accountability.

With offerings, the motive is more important than the amount. God operates on maximums, not minimums. We need to give as the Holy Spirit convicts and give with no strings attached—without control. When we try to control the offering, even after we have given it, then we have never really given it. We are only managing our investment somewhere else. We conclude that *"The Lord does not need our offerings. We cannot enrich him by our gifts. Says the psalmist: 'All things come of thee, and of thine own have we given thee.' Yet God permits us to show our appreciation of his mercies by self-sacrificing efforts to extend the same to others. <u>This is the only way in which it is possible for us to manifest our gratitude and love to God. He has provided no other</u>"* (Review and Herald, December 6, 1887).

We now have discovered what it means to put God first. We are ready now to get His counsel on managing the rest of our possessions. We can build upon this foundation a financial structure that will give us satisfaction and financial freedom.

Assignment for this lesson:

1. Memorize Deuteronomy 16:16, 17.
2. Pray for the needs of your group members.
3. Complete the worksheets for this lesson.
4. Renew your covenant with God for financial faithfulness.

Looking at Giving

Memory Text: Deuteronomy 16:16, 17

"They shall not appear before the Lord empty-handed. Every man shall give as he is able, according to the blessing of the Lord your God which He has given you."

PRAYER TIME:

Make a list of those in your group who have asked for special prayer needs this week and pray for them each day.

_____

_____

Pray also for God's wisdom and blessing as you develop your financial plan.

STUDY TIME:

Day One

Read and reflect on 2 Corinthians 9:6-11 and 1 Corinthians 16:1-2.

1. What key principles from these passages should guide our giving? _____

_____

_____

2. Who gives us the ability to give and how should that affect our giving? _____

_____

_____

Read and reflect on 2 Corinthians 8:1-5.

3. What lessons can we learn from the example of the Macedonian churches? _____

_____

Day Two

Read and reflect on Genesis 14:17-20 and 28:10-22.

1. What led to Jacob's commitment to tithe? _____

_____

2. How were Abraham and Jacob's giving of tithe acts of worship? _____

_____

3. How were Abraham and Jacob's tithes a response to the blessings they had already received? _____

_____

Day Three

Read and reflect on Leviticus 27:30-33 and Numbers 18:21-28.

1. In what way is tithe different than an offering to God? _____

_____

2. What principles on tithing can we understand from these passages? _____

_____

Read and reflect on Deuteronomy 12:6-17.

3. What differences are there as to how the tithe in Leviticus and Numbers was to be used as compared

with a different tithe in Deuteronomy? _____

_____

Day Four

Read and reflect on Deuteronomy 16:16; Proverbs 3:9-10; and Acts 20:35.

1. Why is giving important in our relationship with God? _____

_____

_____

2. In what ways do we receive blessings when we give? _____

_____

_____

3. What different kinds of offerings can we give along with money offerings? _____

_____

_____

Day Five

Read and reflect on Malachi 2:17-3:12.

1. What does it mean to "return" to God in Malachi 3:7? _____

_____

_____

2. Why is failure to return the tithe and give our offerings to God robbery? _____

_____

_____

3. Why can we not truly enjoy our material possessions if we are robbing God?

_____

_____

Day Six

Read and reflect on Deuteronomy 12:10, 11; Deuteronomy 16:16, 17, and Psalms 122:1-4.

1. What reasons can you think of for a central storehouse? _____

_____

_____

2. Why was in necessary for the men of Israel to travel all the way to Jerusalem three times a year to deliver their tithes and offerings? _____

_____

_____

3. Explain the command of God, "Do not appear before the Lord empty-handed." _____

_____

_____

Debt-free Living

Memory Text: Proverbs 22:7

"The rich rules over the poor, and the borrower is servant to the lender."

The problem seemed insignificant—just a small leak in an underground city tunnel. City council employees knew about this minor water leakage. They had shot pictures of it, completed the necessary forms, filed them with the appropriate departments, and even discussed how they were going to repair this problem. What happened next caught them and the whole city of Chicago by surprise. Over 250 million gallons of local river water gushed through the downtown business district, resulting in over $300 million in flood damages!

While the city of Chicago engineers learned a valuable lesson from that 1992 flood, our nation has not acknowledged that it has a problem far worse than a small water leak. This country is being swamped by a flood of debt—national and private.

Currently, the United States has run up a huge mountain of debt of over $11 trillion, which equals about $36,000 for every man, woman and child in our country! (Interestingly, the total national debt in 1837 was $38,000, which is roughly equal the proportionate debt of each person in America today.)

However, that's only half the story. The average American family is drowning in debt. About 43% of American families spend more than they earn each year. Average households carry over $8,000 in credit card debt. The combined total of unpaid credit card debt carried over each month for Americans is now just over $915 billion! Personal bankruptcies have doubled in the last decade. And 10 million families have mortgages exceeding the current value of their homes. Banks are failing, and those still in business are having to cope with borrowers who are defaulting in droves on mortgages, consumer debt, credit cards, student loans, home equity loans, and car loans.

Simply put, we are in very big trouble! It would be wonderful to believe that we as Christians were immune from running our finances in the red. Unfortunately, surveys indicate we are in as much trouble as those who do not profess Christian principles! So the question often asked is, "Just how does the average individual or family find himself/themselves in this debt situation?" Here are a few suggestions why debt is growing in this country:

1. Consumptive lifestyle

Americans are spending at a rate never before seen by previous generations. In a recent year our savings rate was a negative number. This means that families spent all of their income and then some. There are a variety of reasons for this. First of all, there is the sheer variety of items offered in any departmental store, supermarket, or on the Internet. For example, there are 125 brands of yogurt, 184 kinds of breakfast cereal, and 250 types of toothpastes. Secondly, there is the purchasing of lots of non-essential items, because they are fun to buy or are bargains. It is easy to forget that bargains are such only if you need the item in the first place. Finally, how can an individual not spend when the lifestyle philosophy of this current generation has as its theme, "We don't believe in delayed gratification," and economic slogans like "Enjoy it now," "You only go around once," "Live it up," and "You owe it to yourself"? Many live like everything is a need rather than a want or desire.

Suggested Solution: The truth is that very few of our daily purchases are need-based. The majorities are founded on desires and wants. Keep to a philosophy of "need-based spending" by having a written list of the items you need to buy. This is especially helpful if you are purchasing household items. Otherwise, you may end up purchasing non-essentials just because they are on sale. Also, setting a limit on the amount you wish to spend is important, especially on major items such as clothing and furniture.

2. Ease of credit

The ease at which the average person can acquire credit today would amaze previous generations. Each year American families are bombarded by credit card applications—approximately two mail solicitations per week—and we take the bait on so many of them! Once we have signed up with a particular credit card company, it will regularly send us checks that can be used from our credit card account. Many of our high charge and credit card balances are a result of a department store's initial 10% discount on the first purchase. After that it is easy to continue using plastic without considering whether or not the money for this purchase is in the household budget.

Not only is it easy to borrow money, but also many times a financial institution will offer loans up to 125% of the equity of your home!

At the end of 2007 it was reported that Americans were currently carrying over $900 billion in credit card debt. At about the same time I counseled with a Christian couple in their early 60s who had credit cards from eleven different entities and carried a balance of $182,500!

Suggested Solution: If credit cards are a financial downfall, then the accounts should be closed and the cards destroyed. Have a family ceremony in which you destroy your credit cards, similar to the public burning of the scrolls of sorcery by the early Christians at Ephesus (Acts 19:18-20). Purchasing a paper shredder would be a sure and safe investment. Not only would you be able to cut up those high interest checks, but also you would be assured that they would not fall into the hands of a financial thief.

3. Adult toys

Drive down any street in a middle-class American neighborhood and you will see parked outside a variety of adult financial toys, such as recreational vehicles, pleasure boats, motorcycles, jet skis, and snow mobiles to name a few. Often we change our vehicles for reasons other than age or high repair bills. For example, we like the sleek lines of the current model, the smell of the new upholstery, because of peer pressure or the excuse, "My clients expect it." Boiled down, these are poor excuses for trying to keep up with the Joneses and really are based on plain self-gratification and ego.

Suggested Solution: Change your vehicle for the right reasons, such as safety and security for your family or just plain economics. Realizing your vehicle is in the auto repair garage more than in yours may signify the need to look for a new (or at least different) car.

4. Eating out

A common practice among both adults and teenagers is eating out. In a recent USDA's nationwide survey, it was reported that 70% of teenage males ate out on an average day and the percentage of household food moneys spent on meals eaten away from home averaged 40% plus! This overspending of our entertainment allowance every week results in both a super-sized generation as well as less money for other essentials. Studies have shown that eating out just one meal per day will double the money spent monthly on the food budget!

Suggested Solution: Save the treat of eating out for special occasions such as birthdays and romantic dates. Simplify your meals without losing

5. Unexpected bills

There are three areas of spending that cause many families to get into financial trouble. These include motor vehicles—purchase, repair, and maintenance; medical expenses; and household expenses beyond the mortgage payment such as taxes, insurance and maintenance. Many times it seems that when it comes to these three areas, it "not only rains, it pours!" On one day the car battery dies, the clothes dryer decides that hot is not its favorite cycle, and one of the youngsters needs to go to the emergency clinic.

Suggested Solution: To be prepared for dealing with these unexpected debts, develop an emergency account with a minimum of $1,000. This is only the starting point for emergency savings. How do you develop an emergency account? Simply set aside $20 or more per week or pay period, and let it grow until you have enough to cover those sudden financial "surprises." You might even jump-start the account by using the proceeds from your annual raise or your income tax refund check. Some financial educators call it a "freedom account" and it is truly that. You will no longer have to worry about those unexpected bills, because the money will already be available.

6. Reduction in income

A reduction in household income can be due to a variety of reasons such as the loss in employment by one spouse, chronic illness, or a family crisis. Many times it happens unexpectedly such as employment termination due to a corporate takeover, downsizing, or natural disaster.

Suggested Solution: One of the first rules of financial planning is to have three or more month's worth of living expenses (after taxes) set aside for those long-term emergencies. The best way to prepare for these situations is to save a fixed dollar amount each month until you have obtained your three-month minimum goal.

7. Lack of household budget or spending plan

People overspend for a variety of reasons, but the two primary reasons are 1) they do not have a financial plan or budget or 2) they have a very flexible or elastic one and seldom stick to it.

Suggested Solution: If you are experiencing difficulty with your money management, set up a family budget. It can be as simple as totaling all your expenditures for two or three months and then averaging your monthly expenses. Next, compare your expenses to the spendable income you received for the same period of time. If your expenses are higher than your income, then you need financial first aid. A budget can be one of the most freeing things you can develop as an individual or as a family. There are many practical books on budgeting that you can purchase as well as a number of computer software programs that are designed to help you establish a budget and then track your expenses. We will cover the development of a simple budget specifically in the next chapter.

THE BIBLICAL PERSPECTIVE ON DEBT

Although today debt seems to be part of the American economy and way of life, it should never be the norm for Christians. The Bible says "NO" to debt. In the Scriptures, there are at least twenty-six references to debt; and all are negative. It does not say it is a sin to borrow money, but it does talk about the consequences of doing so. Here are seven Biblical principles about indebtedness.

1. Debt—a form of bondage

"The borrower is servant to the lender" (Proverbs 22:7).

In the time of the patriarchs, more often than not, the individual became a slave precisely because he or she was a debtor. Not much has changed in four thousand years. Admittedly, we are no longer thrown into physical bondage, but too often we have become slaves to material possessions through over extension of credit.

The best advice about borrowing to avoid that bondage is to always follow these three rules:

- Borrow only on items that <u>appreciate in value</u>
- Borrow with a <u>short-term loan</u>
- Borrow at the <u>best interest rate available</u>

2. Debt—a lack of contentment

"I have learned in whatever state I am, to be content" (Philippians 4:11). And Paul told the young man, Timothy, *"Now godliness with contentment is great gain. For we brought nothing into this world, and it is certain we can carry nothing out. And having food and clothing, with these we shall be content"* (1 Timothy 6:6-8).

A lack of financial contentment is often reflected in our modern society in the attitudes we have toward debt. It can take the form of "keeping up with the Joneses," desiring what others have (covetousness), or wanting more than we already have (greediness). Frequently people are willing to go into debt to satisfy these desires.

3. Debt presumes on the future

"Now listen, you who say, Today or tomorrow we will go to this or that city, spend a year there, carry on business and make money. Why, you do not even know what will happen tomorrow" (James 4:13-16).

Up until World War II, few Americans carried loans over an extended period. In 1939, Congress for the first time enacted a law allowing the general public to procure twenty-five year home mortgages. Previously the longest home loans were six years, and car loans were no longer than one year. Today in America, you can get home loans up to forty years! (Only the Japanese out-loan us with 100-year mortgages.) In addition, we now can procure home equity loans that even exceed the amount we have in residential value by thousands of dollars. Yet in all of this, many do not know if they can make the next payment.

4. Avoid Get-Rich-Quick Schemes

"A faithful man will abound with blessings, but he who makes haste to be rich will not go unpunished" (Proverbs 28:20). *"But those who desire to be rich fall into temptation and a snare, and into many foolish and harmful lusts which drown men in destruction and perdition. For the love of money is the root of all kinds of evil, for which some have strayed from the faith in their greediness, and pierced themselves through with many sorrows"* (1 Timothy 6:9, 10).

Get-rich-quick schemes flourish when two elements are present. One element is a person or persons who wishes to profit financially from the ignorance, naiveté, and greed of others. The other is the desire on the part of a person or persons to strike it rich with little effort and big dreams. When these two meet, there is a big flash in the pan that quickly dies out. Many people are hurt emotionally and financially, and friendships end. An additional tragedy with these devious plans is that in most cases, individuals have to borrow money to become involved. And when the scheme fails, they not only lose the money borrowed, but also often have to pay it back at high interest, thus putting the family under financial strain.

5. Refuse to be surety for others

The Bible is very clear that we should not become responsible for the debt obligation of others. Four times the inspired wise man, Solomon, warned against surety:

"My son, if you become surety for your friend, if you have shaken hands in pledge for a stranger, you are snared by the words of your own mouth; you are taken by the words of your mouth. So do this, my son, and deliver yourself; for you have come into the hand of your friend: go and humble yourself; plead with your friend. Give no sleep to your eyes, nor slumber to your eyelids. Deliver yourself like a gazelle from the hand of the hunter, and like a bird from the hand of the fowler" (Proverbs 6:1-5).

"He who is surety for a stranger will suffer for it, but one who hates being surety is secure" (Proverbs 11:15).

"A man devoid of understanding shakes hands in a pledge, and becomes surety for his friend" (Proverbs 17:18).

"Do not be one of those who shakes hands in a pledge, one of those who is surety for debts" (Proverbs 22:26).

Surety usually occurs when a person with poor credit seeks a loan from a lending institution and does not qualify for the loan. The loan officer will tell the unqualified person that if he will get a friend with good credit to co-sign with him, then the bank will grant the loan and hold the co-signer responsible in the event of default.

Sometimes a fellow church member will come to you and ask you to co-sign for him. Your response should be, "The Bible says I should never do that." Please understand that the Bible encourages us to be helpful to those in need, but we should not become responsible for their debts.

Parents are often asked by teenagers to co-sign for the purchase of their first car. Or older adult children will ask the parents to co-sign for a business loan. The same answer applies. It is appropriate to help others if you see a real need, but do not become surety for the debts of others. The Bible says this is a mistake. According to the Federal Trade Commission, 75% of those who co-signed for finance company loans end up making the payments (*U. S. News & World Report*, February 14, 2000).

6. Debt can erode our Christian witness

"The wicked borrow and do not repay" (Psalms 37:21).It is impossible to tell your landlord that Jesus loves him and is the answer to all his problems when he is thinking why has your Jesus not convicted you to pay up your last two months rent. A century ago, Ellen White put it this way: *"You bring a reproach upon the cause by locating in a place where you indulge for a time and then are obliged to run in debt for provision for your family. These are your honest debts you are not always particular to pay, but, instead move to another place. This is defrauding your neighbor. The world has a right to expect strict integrity in those who profess to be Bible Christians"* (*Testimonies for the Church*, vol. 5, p.179).

7. Debt imperils one's giving

"Every man shall give as he is able, according to the blessing of the Lord your God which He has given you" (Deuteronomy 16:17).

As we look at annual statistics about charitable contributions in our society, what should always surprise and shock us is that the giving pattern between Christians and non-Christians is approximately the same—about 2.5%. Perhaps the biggest reason that the average American Christian does not return the 10% that God asks him to give—even though the Bible promises spiritual and physical blessings for doing so—is that he is over his head in debt. In addition, many have never learned the Biblical principles of tithing.

Red Flags

Here are some red flags which may help you assess whether or not you are falling into the debtor's pit:

Regularly paying bills late—*This would include the following:*

a. You write out your checks for this month's bills but do not post them, because you do not have enough money in your bank to cover all of them.

b. You constantly are figuring out how to make next month's paycheck cover this month's bills.

c. You pay only half the regular bills this month and leave the rest, hoping you will have enough money next month to cover the other half.

d. You consider any account that is thirty days late as on time, and you never pay a bill before its due date; you may need that payment for a more pressing need.

e. You pay late fees regularly.

Consistently living on credit—*This would include the following:*

a. When you need or use more than two credit cards, you are living above your means.

b. When the balance on your credit cards is consistently increasing, you are surviving on credit.

c. When you apply for a new credit card to get through another month or to pay the minimum balance on your previous cards, you definitely exist on credit.

d. When you never are able to pay cash for

even a fast food lunch or a few items at the corner store, this indicates you are rapidly becoming a credit junky.

An inconsistent giver—*This would include the following:*

a. You believe in returning your tithe and offerings to the Lord—and will gladly do so when you have enough to cover your regular expenses.

b. You consider the payment of your children's Christian education as your way of returning tithe to the Lord or paying your share of the local church budget.

c. You argue that the many hours of volunteer time you give to charity and/or the local church is equivalent to giving financially to God's work.

Worry constantly about finances—*This would include the following:*

a. When you are awake, you cannot think of anything else but your money troubles, and when you should be getting a good night's sleep, you suffer from insomnia because of your many financial obligations.

b. When the phone rings you are afraid to answer it, because it will be another demanding creditor advising you to pay up or else!

c. You are constantly thinking of new places to hide purchases that your spouse would not approve.

In a recent year, credit card issuers in the United States stuffed mailboxes with more than 7 billion offers. Debt is now the most highly advertised commodity in Western society! As you would expect, people, businesses, and even governments are accepting the offers of credit and sinking deeper and deeper into debt-bondage. Personal bankruptcies are at an all-time high with more than 30,000 U. S. families filing for bankruptcy protection every week! The Bible equates debt with bondage and slavery (Proverbs 22:7). If we incur a debt, we are duty-bound to repay it (Psalms 37:21). Interest is one expense you can live without.

Instead of using words or phrases such as "over your head," "hard up," "in the red," "mortgaged to the hilt," that relate to how much further you will be in debt should you accept their offer, the credit card companies instead use flattering and manipulative words and phrases such as "you deserve it," "cash advances when needed," "do with it as you please," and "it makes life easier."

Credit card issuers make their profits from lending lots of money and charging hefty fees to families that are financially strapped. More than 75% of credit card profits come from people who make low, minimum monthly payments. Who makes minimum payments at 26% interest? Who pays late fees, over balance charges, and cash advance premiums? They are families who can barely make ends meet and households precariously balanced between financial survival and complete collapse.

Credit card debt has now gone over the $900 billion mark in America. If you want something to worry about, forget about global warming and get concerned about the financial tsunami that is building in the sea of credit card debt. It is a much more certain reality.

Steps to getting out and staying out of debt

1. Make a decision. Recognize the problem. Decide to become debt-free!

The most difficult thing to do when you are in over your head in debt is to admit to yourself that you are out of control and you need to change your attitude about spending. This is the time to be absolutely honest concerning what caused your debt situation. You cannot change your behavior or your situation unless you identify and deal with the root problem. To make debt disappear requires money management discipline and reordering your life style priorities. You may wish there were an easier way, but those who have fallen into the debt pit know from personal experience, there "just isn't."

2. Seek Divine help.

Make your financial decision a matter of spiritual commitment. Ask for God's forgiveness and guidance. Ask for God's strength to help carry out your decision. God can and will help you and your family along the road to debt-free living. Make a covenant with God—a promise in prayer—that you will use His blessings to pay off your debts.

3. Discontinue all credit purchases.

Simply stop going further into debt! Decide you will <u>not</u> borrow for <u>any</u> purpose! Close your store-brand credit cards accounts, and then pay them off as quickly as possible.

4. Determine your current over-all financial situation.

One of the most prominent factors of many individuals in financial trouble is that they have no idea how much they owe—or worse, what exorbitant interest they are paying. So sit down and list all the amounts you owe on your home, credit cards, vehicle and student loans, department store credit lines, etc. Be absolutely honest in terms of the total amount you or your family owes. This exercise will give you the true picture of your debt situation and motivate you to become debt free. For assistance with this determination, consult your Balance Sheet completed for Lesson #2.

5. Develop a repayment plan.

It is very tempting—and the rationale makes sense—to get a debt consolidation loan. But for many this has been the means of getting deeper into debt. Many families have used a debt consolidation loan to pay off credit cards and other short-term loans. This plan does not eliminate the debt, of course, but simply stretches it out for a much longer period of time to produce a lower monthly payment. As a result, much more interest is paid over the life of the loan. The trap in this method is that once the credit cards are paid off, many people start using the cards again and eventually max out their cards again. Only this time, they have the long-term debt consolidation loan as well.

At this point, we would recommend that you follow this simple plan:

Establish the tithe

It bears repeating that God's blessing attends those families that are faithful with God's tithe. What family could afford to be without God's wisdom and blessing? How could we expect the blessing of God when we are robbing Him? Lay the financial foundation of faithfulness to God, and then you can do what you can to eliminate the debt with His blessing.

Snowball your debt

One of the best methods to get out of debt recommended by many financial planners and educators is termed "snowballing your debt." The first step in this debt reduction strategy is to list all your consumer debts in ascending order with the largest balance in the top spot and the smallest amount that you owe at the bottom. Follow this strategy, unmindful of the interest rates of your debt balances. The purpose of this plan is to experience the joy of quick success by paying off the smallest debt first.

For example, for many families their largest debt is their home mortgage loan with thousands of dollars outstanding. Their lowest obligation is a local department store charge card totaling $120. Following this plan, you must pay the minimum payment due to each debt every month. However, the debt at the bottom of your list gets your primary reduction focus. In addition to its minimum payment, you gather all the money you can from every source, including any windfalls that you get, and put it on the high priority debt. As soon as it is paid off, focus on the next debt, etc. Once Number 2 account is paid, attack Number 3, and so on. You and your family will be very blessed and thrilled as you see the debts liquidated.

Many are tempted to pay on the home mortgage first after learning how much interest they can save by pre-paying the principle. This is not a good idea for two reasons. First, the interest you pay on the home mortgage is still tax deductible as no other consumer interest is. Second, the home mortgage is the largest debt and would take a comparatively long time to pay off. Meanwhile you still would be paying high interest on your smaller bills.

Like a snowball that picks up more snow as it rolls down the hill, your extra cash will increase with each payoff. By the time you reach that final account, you will have an avalanche of extra cash. Soon you finally will be debt free! (A form is provided at the end of this lesson for visualizing your debt and dealing with it.)

To make "snowballing your debt" work, you unwaveringly MUST follow these steps:

- First and most important, draw a line in your "financial sand" and say, "I/we will not borrow again until all my/our current debts are completely paid off."
- Develop a new balanced household budget that includes all living expenses PLUS all your debts.
- Keep focused on your goal of getting out of debt. You cannot wander aimlessly in your intention to be debt-free. It must be your burning desire!
- When you prayerfully determine to win the victory over debt, it will surprise you how God will pour out His blessings to help you accomplish your goal in an even shorter period of time.

Remember, the bottom line is to quit spending more money than you earn. If your situation is critical—you are getting calls from creditors, your car has been repossessed, or you are facing bankruptcy—then you should get personal help from a debt-counselor or assistance from CCCS (Consumer Credit Counseling Service). Or contact the CROWN financial counselor (www.crown.org) in your area.

Once you have made the decision to become debt free and have followed the steps listed above, you would do well to contact any creditors where you may have been late making a payment or in some manner have gotten behind. Let them know that you are working on the problem and plan to pay the debt in a timely manner.

Declare your accountability

To avoid a debt relapse, put your commitment to being debt-free and your debt-reduction plan in writing. Report monthly by phone to a trusted friend, a prayer partner, or your financial counselor at church. This does not mean that the person has to know the details of your debt or accept the responsibility for your debt. He is not your financial jailer! However, accountability is a key to your success in this program of getting out and staying out of financial trouble. It could be as simple as saying to your local church pastor as you shake hands with him at the church door, "We did it again." That way, only the pastor and you will know about this important commitment. There is a better life after debt!

What About Bankruptcy?

Bankruptcy law provides for the development of a plan that allows a debtor who is unable to pay his creditors to resolve his debts through the division of his assets among his creditors. This supervised division also allows the interests of all creditors to be treated with some measure of equality. An additional purpose of bankruptcy law is to allow certain debtors to free themselves (to be discharged) of the financial obligations they have accumulated after their assets are distributed, even if their debts have not been paid in full.

Bankruptcy law is federal statutory law contained in Title 11 of the United States Code. Bankruptcy proceedings are supervised by and litigated in the United States Bankruptcy Courts. These courts are a part of the District Courts of the United States.

There are two basic types of bankruptcy proceedings. A filing under Chapter 7 is called liquidation. It is the most common type of bankruptcy proceeding. Liquidation involves the appointment of a trustee who collects the non-exempt property of the debtor, sells it, and distributes the proceeds to the creditors. Bankruptcy proceedings under Chapters 11, 12, and 13 involve the rehabilitation of the debtor to allow him or her to use future earnings to pay off creditors. Under Chapter 7, 12, 13, and some 11 proceedings, a trustee is appointed to supervise the assets of the debtor.

A bankruptcy proceeding either can be entered into voluntarily by a debtor or initiated by creditors. After a bankruptcy proceeding is filed, creditors, for the most part, may not seek to collect their debts outside of the proceeding. The debtor is not allowed to transfer property that has been declared part of the estate subject to proceedings. Furthermore, certain pre-proceeding transfers of property, secured interests, and liens may be delayed or invalidated.

Passage of the Bankruptcy Prevention and Consumer Protection Act in April 2005 has resulted in major reforms in bankruptcy law, outlining revised guidelines governing the dismissal or conversion of Chapter 7 liquidations to Chapter 11 or 13 proceedings. The law also expands the responsibilities of the United States Trustees Program to include supervision of random and targeted audits, certification of entities to provide credit counseling that individuals must receive before filing for bankruptcy, certification of entities that provide financial education to individuals before being discharged from debt, and greater oversight of small business Chapter 11 reorganization cases.

One can file for bankruptcy protection only once every seven years. The fact that a person has bankrupted stays on his credit report for ten years and may affect him for life on such items as loan applications and acceptance into professional organizations such as state bar associations.

People frequently ask, "Isn't bankruptcy provided for in the Bible?" The answer is "No!" The verse frequently referred to is Deuteronomy 15:1, 2. *"At the end of every seven years you shall grant a release of debts. And this is the form of the release: Every creditor who has lent anything to his neighbor shall release it; he shall not require it of his neighbor or his brother, because it is called the LORD's release."* This counsel was given to creditors, not debtors. It was simply God's way of limiting long-term indebtedness to a maximum of seven years! And as we have already noted, *"The wicked borrows and does not repay, but the righteous shows mercy and gives"* (Psalms 37:21).

The bankruptcy laws were put in place to help those who faced catastrophic or overwhelming circumstances. But many today have abused the bankruptcy system because of their personal poor management. For the sake of Christian witness and credit integrity, we rarely would recommend bankruptcy and would encourage the reorganization method at that point.

Frequently when a family is over its head in credit card debt, it will be bombarded by offers to "lower your monthly payments" by taking a second mortgage or cashing out the equity from the home. Don't do it! Refinancing the home to pay down other bills is the single biggest mistake made by a family in trouble.

If you are in financial trouble, you probably will be steered into a high-cost, subprime mortgage, making any gains illusory. Worst of all, you will be jeopardizing the roof over your family's head. If the mortgage lender gives you a lower rate than the credit card company, it is because the mortgage lender gets something in return—the right to push you into the street, seize your home, and sell it.

If your financial troubles get bad enough, you can file for bankruptcy to eliminate your high-interest credit card debts and cash advances, but bankruptcy cannot help with a home equity loan or a refinanced mortgage. You must pay the mortgage lender in full (plus all penalties, late fees, and interest) or face foreclosure. The chance to save a few dollars a month on your credit card bills is not worth running the risk that you will not have a place to live.

Remember that in all states, the creditors who have security interests—the home mortgage company and the car lender, for example—must be paid if the family wants to hold on to these assets. And some debts are never forgiven, no matter what. Taxes, student loans, alimony, and child support must be paid in full regardless of how long it takes. Bankruptcy offers no relief whatsoever to these obligations.

Some Counsel from the Last Century

"Be determined never to incur another debt. Deny yourself a thousand things rather than run in debt. This has been the curse of your life, getting into debt. Avoid it as you would the smallpox.

"Make a solemn covenant with God that by His blessing you will pay your debts and then owe no man anything if you live on porridge and bread. It is so easy in preparing your table to throw out of your pocket twenty-five cents for extras. Take care of the pennies, and the dollars will take care of themselves. It

is the mites here and the mites there that are spent for this, that, and the other that soon run up into dollars. Deny self at least while you are walled in with debts. … Do not falter, be discouraged, or turn back. Deny your taste, deny the indulgence of appetite, save your pence, and pay your debts. Work them off as fast as possible. When you can stand forth a free man again, owing no man anything, you will have achieved a great victory" (The Adventist Home, p. 393).

Take Responsibility

No matter what contributed to your current financial condition, you will have little possibility of making the necessary changes and becoming a dependable money manager if you do not take full responsibility for your situation. Too many individuals use the following excuses for their lack of responsibility:

- My spouse is a spender, so I have no hope of staying out of debt as long as we are married.
- I know having a household budget is important if we are going to get out of debt. But we tried it once and it just didn't work for us.
- I don't understand it. My parents/in-laws have tons and tons of money, yet they never lift a hand to help us.

Instead of blaming your spouse, your parents or in-laws, or your lack of financial discipline, own up to your own responsibility to pay your creditors. Mary Hunt wrote, "Instead of slamming the phone on your creditors, destroying the bills that come in the mail, and doing everything you can to avoid facing the music, stop running. Accept the calls, do the right thing, learn the truth, get it down in writing, inhale deeply, and take responsibility" (Money Matters, August 1998).

Lessons from a President— Ulysses S. Grant

One of America's great military presidents was Ulysses S. Grant, whose adult life could be divided into three major sections. First was his military career,

where he distinguished himself as a combat officer. Secondly, he distinguished himself as President of the United States, where, in his first term in office, he enacted and ratified the Fifteenth Amendment banning discrimination in voting rights.

However, it is in the third segment of his life that we truly learn about this great man's character. In New York as a private citizen, Ulysses Grant invested his life savings in a brokerage partnership with Frederick Ward, which unfortunately left him with a debt of $150,000 after the Wall Street panic of 1884. To make ends meet, he penned three articles about his Civil War experiences for Century Magazine in a series entitled, "Battles and Leaders."

While writing these articles for Century Magazine, Grant learned that he had incurable throat cancer. To pay off his creditors and to support his family after his death, he signed a contract with the new Mark Twain Publishing Company for 70% of the net proceeds of the sale of his personal life story. Despite intense pain, Grant wrote chapter after chapter, completing the last one just a few days before his death at Mount McGregor. The Personal Memoirs of U. S. Grant had extraordinary sales, paying off his debt and leaving over $300,000 for his wife and family.

This president's life story is in sharp contrast to the more than 1.5 million Americans who will renege on their debts and declare bankruptcy during this year.

There is no more secure investment than your own debts. Even if your current debts are very manageable, it is wise to pre-pay all debts so that you can hasten the day when your family will be debt free.

Assignment for this lesson:

1. Memorize Proverbs 22:7.
2. Complete the worksheets for this lesson.
3. List all of your debts on Form #4 included with this lesson.
4. Determine that by the grace of God, you/your family will be debt free.

Lesson 4 Worksheets

Looking at Debt

Memory text: Proverbs 22:7

"The rich rules over the poor, and the borrower is servant to the lender."

PRAYER TIME:

Make a list of those in your group who have asked for special prayer needs this week and pray for them each day.

_____

_____

Pray also for God's wisdom and blessing as you develop your financial plan.

STUDY TIME:

Day One

Read and reflect on Proverbs 22:7

1. How does the Bible portray a person who gets into debt? _____

_____

_____

2. What does it mean to be a "servant" to the lender? _____

_____

_____

3. Some Bible versions translate *servant* as *slave*. In what way is debt like bondage? _____

_____

_____

4. Fill out Form #4 that is included with this lesson. You can use the balance sheet from Lesson 2 (Form #2) for assistance to remember your debts (liabilities) for this exercise. Don't be discouraged when you see your totals. This exercise allows you to visualize your debt so that you can put a plan into action to control and eliminate all your debts.

Faith and Finance: Financial Planning with a Faith Factor   **53**   *A 12 lesson practical study on money management*

Day Two

Read and reflect on Romans 13:8

1. How does this passage apply to your mortgage, school or vehicle loan? _____

_____

_____

_____

_____

2. This scriptural text seems to indicate borrowing money always has a negative effect on your finances.

Do you agree or disagree? Explain: _____

_____

_____

_____

_____

Day Two

Read and reflect on Psalms 37:21.

1. What are people called that do not repay their debts? _____

_____

_____

2. Why are they given this name? _____

_____

_____

3. By implication from this verse, what do the righteous do with their debts? _____

_____

_____

4. With this verse in mind, how should a Christian view bankruptcy? _____

_____

_____

_____

Day Three

Read and reflect on Deuteronomy 15:1, 2.

1. Is this Bible passage talking about bankruptcy? Explain. _____

   _____

   _____

   _____

2. What wording in this passage is similar to what you know about bankruptcy? _____

   _____

   _____

   _____

3. To what type of person is this passage addressed? Debtors or creditors? _____

   _____

   _____

   _____

4. Why would God want to limit long-term indebtedness to a maximum of 7 years? _____

   _____

   _____

   _____

Day Four

Read and reflect on Proverbs 6:1-5; 11:15; 17:18; and 22:26.

1. What is *surety* and why does the Bible warn us against it? _____

   _____

   _____

   _____

2. But isn't it all right to co-sign for family and friends? (See Proverbs 17:18). _____

   _____

   _____

   _____

3. What is it about co-signing that makes it so risky and dangerous? _____

_____

_____

_____

(Note: If you co-sign for someone to get a loan, that loan is on your credit report until it is completely paid off. Remember that we should be willing to help others, but the Bible says that we should not become responsible for their debts.)

Day Five

Read and reflect on Deuteronomy 28:9-13 and compare with verses 43-45 of the same chapter.

1. What promises concerning debt does God make to those who obey His commandments? _____

_____

_____

_____

2. What financial condition could we find ourselves in if we don't follow God's commandments? _____

_____

_____

_____

Read and reflect on Matthew 5:42.

3. Does this passage mean that we should lend to any person in need? Explain your answer. _____

_____

_____

_____

4. What factors or principles should we keep in mind when considering lending money to another person

or family? _____

_____

_____

_____

Day Six

Read and reflect on 2 Kings 4:1-7.

1. What is the general attitude of creditors toward those who owe them money? (What do you think your credit card company thinks of you?) _____

_____

_____

_____

2. What should a Christian do when faced with a debt crisis? _____

_____

_____

_____

3. How could the key points of this story be applied to us today? _____

_____

_____

_____

Read and reflect on Exodus 22:25 and Leviticus 25:35-37.

4. How does God consider the poor, and what is our responsibility toward them? _____

_____

_____

_____

5. Is it appropriate to charge interest on loans to those who are not poor? Explain. _____

_____

_____

_____

6. What debt can never be repaid? (See Romans 13:8) _____

_____

_____

Debt Visualization

(Photocopy and make additional sheets if needed)

Examples	Our Debts (name) (List largest down to smallest)	Balance Pay Off	Monthly Min. Payment
Home Mortgage			
2nd Mortgage			
Line of Credit			
Student Loans			
Car Loans			
Personal Loan			
Credit Cards			
Other Debts			
TOTALS			

Lesson 5

Developing a Spending Plan

Memory Text: Psalms 1:1-3

"Blessed is the man who walks not in the counsel of the ungodly, nor stands in the path of sinners, nor sits in the seat of the scornful; But his delight is in the law of the LORD, and in His law he meditates day and night. He shall be like a tree planted by the rivers of water, that brings forth its fruit in its season, whose leaf also shall not wither; and whatever he does shall prosper."

If the threat of dirty bombs, bird flu and global warming is not enough to keep you up at night, now researchers are warning of looming financial disaster for the young adults of today. The fact is, according to them, in spite of their material trappings, from iPods, iPhones, and Xboxes, today's young people are behind the proverbial eight ball. The idea of struggling financially in the post-student days is nothing new. The problem according to the researchers is that those days—those lean early years—may never give way to the stability and prosperity enjoyed by their boomer parents.

A number of factors are blamed for this dismal picture. The primary ones are student loans, credit cards, wage stagnation, the rising cost of health care and housing, and the disappearance of pensions along with the plight of Social Security. These factors lead to a delayed entry into marriage and parenting and a widening gap between the rich and poor.

Sticking to a budget means financial discipline today for the sake of one's future well-being. Few have the discipline that this requires. Instead it's dine at expensive restaurants, buy new cars every two or three years, and spend $3.00 or more on smoothies or hot drinks while shopping. Result? Even people with decent incomes live from paycheck to paycheck.

What is a person or family to do in planning for today and the future? The purpose of this lesson is to answer that question. We believe that with proper training, understanding, planning, and implementation, these problems can be managed or avoided altogether.

In the past, financial planners and teachers would have addressed this lesson as "Developing a Budget." But we prefer a "spending plan" approach because of the negative connotation of a budget for most people. Because of the effort necessary to develop a budget, the will power needed to stay on the budget, and the perceived restrictions of a budget, many people equate budgeting to dieting or a trip to the dentist. However, when a budget is viewed as a "spending plan," it actually becomes an avenue to freedom rather than restriction and serves as a vehicle to live well in the present and plan prudently for the future.

Maintaining control over your credit-spending habits will contribute to your financial goals. The overuse or misuse of credit may cause a situation in which a person's debts far exceed the resources available to pay those debts. The people who declare bankruptcy each year might have avoided this trauma with wise spending and borrowing decisions.

Financial planning is designed not to prevent your enjoyment of life but to help you to obtain the things you want or need. Too often, however, people make purchases without considering the financial consequences. Some people shop compulsively, creating financial difficulties. Since the main source of financial difficulties is overspending, spending less than you earn is the only way to achieve long-term financial security.

Starting at the Beginning

Since we are studying the Biblical principles of money management, we will follow the Biblical counsel. Solomon was inspired to write, *"Trust in the Lord with all your heart, and lean not on your own understanding; In all your ways acknowledge Him, and He shall direct your paths. Do not be wise in your own eyes; fear the Lord and depart from evil. It will be health to your flesh, and strength to your bones. Honor the Lord with your possessions, and with the firstfruits of all your increase; So your barns will be filled with plenty, and your vats will overflow with new wine"* (Proverbs 3:5-10).

God asks us to put Him first, not because He needs the money (He does not, see Psalms 50:12), but because He wants to bless the rest and reward our faithful action. Christ Himself reiterated the management principle of putting God first in His Sermon on the Mount. After acknowledging that people had legitimate needs regarding food, clothing, and shelter, He stated, *"Therefore do not worry, saying, 'What shall we eat?' or 'What shall we drink?' or 'What shall we wear?' For after all these*

things the Gentiles seek. For your heavenly Father knows that you need all these things. But seek first the kingdom of God and His righteousness, and all these things shall be added to you" (Matthew 6:31-33).

A budget, or "spending plan," is necessary for successful financial planning. The common financial problems of overusing credit, lacking a savings program, and failing to ensure future financial security can be minimized through budgeting. The main purposes of a budget are to help you:

- Live within your income
- Spend your money wisely
- Reach your financial goals
- Prepare for financial emergencies
- Develop wise financial management habits

Which one of these purposes of a budget would you want to eliminate? It is easy to see from this perspective that a good budget is your friend and not your enemy.

Starting the Budgeting Process

We have prepared a sample budget to use with this chapter. First we will outline the process of filling it out, using it, and modifying it as necessary. We suggest that you do not write on the budget sheet in the book, as it may take several attempts to finally get a budget that fits your specific needs. Just photocopy the one here in the book at work or the library—make several copies—and then you will have the flexibility of developing the budget without "messing up" your book. Note: Your budget, like your balance sheet is for your eyes only and should only be discussed with your leader or counselor as you desire.

Budgeting may be outlined in four major phases. First, assess your current situation. What is the state of your present financial picture? You have already done much of this in Lesson #2 with the preparation of a balance sheet and short and long-range goals. With this information you can determine your personal needs and the direction you want to go financially. Secondly, create your budget percentages and allocations. After tithe, offerings, and taxes, you can begin the process by making good faith estimates. Thirdly, once you have set up your budget, begin to monitor your spending, saving, and investment patterns. Finally, on a quarterly—or at least an annual basis—review your financial progress and revise your budget as income and needs change.

Figuring Your Income

If you get paid once a month, planning is easy, since you will work with a single income amount. But if you get paid weekly or twice a month, you will need to plan how much of each paycheck will go for various expenses. If you get paid every two weeks, plan your spending based on the two paychecks you will receive each month. Then, during the two months each year that you have three paydays, you can put additional amounts into savings, pay off some debts, or make a special purchase.

Budgeting your income takes a little more work if your earnings vary by season or your income is irregular, as with sales commissions. In these situations, attempt to estimate your income based on the past year and on your expectations for the current year. Estimating your income on the low side will help you avoid overspending and other financial difficulties. Note that the income line on the budget is for a monthly amount, so if you are estimating your income for a quarter or a year, you will need to convert that figure to a monthly amount.

Remember, a budget is an estimate for spending and saving that is intended to help you make better use of your money, not to reduce your enjoyment of life. Income is not just your paycheck or salary, but your income from all sources. Your total or gross salary and income is the 100% that is used for the basis of the budget.

Expenses

Tithing is listed first in the expense category because it's a deduction from income that is set aside as holy and belonging to God. For a committed Christian who recognizes the Lordship and Ownership of God, the tithe is always the first item in the expense list. We will repeat, for emphasis, these two important Bible passages. The wisest man who ever lived under the inspiration of the Almighty God recorded in Proverbs 3:9,10, *"Honor the Lord with your possessions, and with the firstfruits of all your increase; so your barns will be filled with plenty, and your vats will overflow with new wine."* And Christ Himself underscored the "God-first" principle in His famous mountainside sermon. *"Therefore do not worry, saying, 'What shall we eat?' or 'What shall we drink?' or 'What shall we wear?' For after all these things the Gentiles seek. For your heavenly Father knows that you need all these things. But seek first the kingdom of God and His righteousness, and all these things shall be added to you"* (Matthew 6:31-33).

So, God has promised in both the Old and New Testaments that if we will put Him first, He will provide for our daily needs. Our faithful tithing demonstrates that we trust God to sustain us and provide for us. This also answers the common question, "Should we tithe on the gross or the net?" When we put God first we tithe on the gross. We frequently tell people who ask this question. "Since God, by His very character and nature is honest, if we give Him too much, He will get it back to us."

Our offerings are not to enrich God. He does not need the money. (see Psalms 50:12). Our offerings are, first of all, an expression of our gratitude to Him for His blessings. So, in the first instance, we do not give to pave the parking lot at church or to buy choir robes, but God encourages us to use our offerings for things that we feel will advance His cause or help others.

We suggest a percentage of 5% for offerings as part of our systematic support of God's work. There is no percentage suggested in the Bible for our offerings, but rather, they are based on how God has blessed us (see Deuteronomy 16:16, 17). Obviously, for those of us who have our children educated, our student loans and mortgages paid off, our offering amounts could and should be much more. This is true because we want to advance the cause of God and store up treasures in heaven.

Income and Social Security Taxes

Please do not get sucked into the scam of not paying taxes. There are numerous books and much bogus information flying around about how the U. S. Constitution does not mandate paying income taxes to the government and that you can opt out if you choose to do so. It's not true. Two examples should suffice to verify this. The notorious Chicago gangster, Al Capone, was likely responsible for the death of over 50 individuals. But his longest prison time, over six years spent in the federal prison at Alcatraz, was based on a conviction for tax evasion.

In November 2007 a former pastor, who operated a "tax consulting" company, agreed to plead guilty to charges of advising others to evade taxes. He faced up to five years in Federal prison and a fine of $250,000. Two of His "clients," who were both medical professionals, failed to file timely income tax returns and faced up to a year in prison and a fine of up to $25,000 each, plus the payment of back taxes with penalties and interest for close to $400,000.

We should all practice tax avoidance, which means that we should take advantage of tax deductions and tax deference (like a 401(k) or 403(b), etc.)—but never engage in tax evasion. From a Biblical perspective, Jesus told us to *"render to Caesar the things that are Caesar's and render to God the things that are God's"* (Matthew 22:21). So, in this part of the budget, determine the amount of taxes that are withheld from your income and enter the amount at the appropriate place on the budget sheet. If you are working for yourself, you will need to estimate the amount and include it here, so you will have the funds to pay the taxes when due.

Savings

Lack of significant savings is one of the major factors in the debt crises in America. A very common budgeting mistake is to spend the amount you have left over at the end of the month. When you do that, you often have nothing left for savings. Since savings are vital to long-term financial security, advisors suggest that an amount for savings be budgeted as an expense item.

How much should a family have in their emergency savings account? A three-month emergency fund is probably adequate for a person with a stable income or secure employment, while a person with erratic or seasonal income may need to set aside an emergency fund sufficient for six months or more of living expenses. This fund is a real lifesaver when unexpected financial situations arise.

Everyone needs a vacation. It is no virtue to brag that you have not had a vacation in ten years.

A vacation allows you to recharge your batteries, make family memories and pictures, and expand your horizons. Unfortunately, many who do take vacations pay for them all year long and end up spending much more than the initial cost when all of the interest is added. A better plan is to save all year long and then pay off your vacation in the process of enjoying it or immediately when you return home. You thereby save lots of money that many families pay in interest.

Sometimes we find young people in the very early stages of their careers quite fixated about saving for retirement. We will discuss this in more detail in Chapters 9 and 10, but please note here that there is no more secure investment than investing in your own debts. If you can pay off all your debt early—student loans, credit cards, automobiles, and even your home—you will be in a much better position to pay for your children's education and to prepare for retirement. In the early stages of your financial planning, do not pass up any free money. What we mean by this is that you should contribute to the full extent of your employer's match to your retirement account. It is not smart to give up free money. This will start your nest egg with your contributions and that of your employer, which can enjoy the "miracle" of compounding interest while you are concentrating on your consumer debt and raising your family.

Fixed Expenses

Housing, whether you own or rent, is for most people the largest single budget item. Shelter is one of man's basic needs. We will give our best information about buying a home in Chapter 7. If you own or are buying a home, then you will have the responsibility of paying property taxes. In most locations this expense comes only once a year, but it can be quite a hit to your budget. Typically, property taxes range from a low of around $500 to over $25,000 per year, depending on the size of the home and where it is located. Almost everyone would need to spread this cost over the entire year. So, as we have discussed about saving for your vacation, set aside some money (1/12th of the estimated amount) each month, so that when the tax bill is due, you will have the money on hand to cover the cost with cash.

You will note on the budget sheet that the next item is Auto loan/Auto savings. This is because your eventual goal will be to pay cash for your automobile purchases. Oh yes, the auto dealer will try to talk you into financing the vehicle (because they get a kickback from the interest charged), but it is always to your advantage to pay cash for reasons we will address in Chapter 7. If you are making time payments on a car now, do not stop the payments when your car is paid off. Simply redirect them into a savings account, so that when the time comes to buy a new car, you will have the money to pay cash. In our society today, transportation is a necessary expense. The best we can do is to buy well, maintain well, and drive well. But the most significant way to save money on transportation costs is to avoid the hundreds and thousands of dollars that many car buyers spend on interest.

Insurance

Insurance is part of what financial planners call risk management. Simply explained, you pay a fee to a company to provide you with an insurance policy, so that in the event of a loss in an accident or injury, you can be made whole. Let us explain. Driving an automobile on the roads around large cities like Washington, D.C. has a certain element of risk to it. Every day on the traffic updates, dozens of wrecks are reported. When these wrecks happen to others, it is no big deal to us. But, if you were involved in an auto accident that was your fault, and there was significant property damage and maybe even someone severely injured or killed, the cost to you to settle a lawsuit against you could wipe you out financially, if you did not have liability insurance. This is one of the reasons automobile liability insurance is required in most, if not all, states.

In another situation, say your house is paid off, lightening comes into your house through your electrical system during a storm, and your house catches on fire and burns down. If you do not have casualty insurance, you just lost the largest single asset in your portfolio. Insurance is what manages that risk. Even if you never need it, you can have the peace of mind that all your hard work is not unprotected. You cannot afford and do not need insurance to cover every eventuality that may occur. You need just basic coverage to insure your largest assets and your health.

Christians and Life Insurance

"What about life insurance?" some ask. "Isn't purchasing insurance a sign of lack of faith in God?" Many investment advisors say that you should not consider life insurance to be a part of your investment portfolio. They say there are better places to put your money for investments. All you need really to manage your risk of premature death is a simple, inexpensive term life insurance policy.

From the close of the Civil War until the end of the century, Ellen White discouraged the purchase of life insurance. However, during the same period, she advocated the purchase of casualty insurance that protected against fire, storm, and theft. She had such insurance on her own home and recommended to the brethren that our churches and administrative buildings also be insured. So, she did not counsel against risk management as such. What she counseled against was the unregulated and frequently fraudulent life insurance policies of the late 19th century.

The Ellen G. White Estate has prepared a document on life insurance that shares the following information regarding such insurance during this period: *"The post Civil War period was a time of rapid expansion in the United States and in technological innovation. It has been described accurately as an age of rampant opportunism and speculation virtually unregulated by the government. Monopolistic practices and industrialization were focused toward the amassing of vast personal fortunes almost untouched by taxes. Get-rich-quick schemes were the order of the day, generally ending in the loss of one's investment. It was a time well characterized by P. T. Barnum's famous quip, 'There's a sucker born every minute.'*

"The fledgling insurance industry was fully involved in the spirit of the times, a spirit steeped in the essence of high risk. Undercapitalized insurance stock groups, while promising quick wealth, frequently collapsed without notice, leaving their policies worthless.

Company dealings with their customers often were unjust and not infrequently fraudulent in nature. Policies written on the lives of complete strangers were urged upon a public that was encouraged to invest in the hope of profiting from the death of the insured.

"The abuses of such a system lead to public demand for government regulation. Beginning in 1906, State and Federal regulatory laws were designed to limit fraud and require the insurance industry to follow sound practices." Following the correction of abuses and the establishment of the legitimate life insurance business as a form of risk management, Ellen White no longer counseled against purchasing life insurance.

Both the Bible and the Spirit of Prophecy teach that it is a divine mandate that the Christian has a responsibility to protect and provide for the needs of his family. The apostle Paul stated this duty in explicit terms: *"But if any widow has children or grandchildren, let them first learn to show piety at home and to repay their parents, for this is good and acceptable before God…But if anyone does not provide for his own, and especially for those of his household, he has denied the faith and is worse than an unbeliever"* (1 Timothy 5:4, 8). Jesus reinforced the same principle of taking care of your immediate family, referring to it as the *"command of God"* (Matthew 15:6).

Accordingly, if you are the primary breadwinner in your family and if you are in debt and you have children to be educated, then, as part of your risk management and your responsibility to provide for your family, you should consider pure life insurance to protect your family in the event of your untimely death. A simple 20-year level-premium, term policy would be adequate to cover the period of time needed to get your house paid off and your children educated. The amount of the policy can be figured using an easy method. Simple as this method is, it is remarkably useful. It is based on the insurance agent's rule of thumb that a "typical family" will need approximately 70% of its salary for seven years to allow it to adjust to the financial consequences of your death.

In other words, for an estimate of your life insurance needs, simply multiply your current gross income by 7 (seven years) and 0.70 (70%). This method assumes your family is "typical." You may need more insurance if you have four or more children, if you have above-average family debt, if any member of your family suffers from poor health, or if your spouse has poor employment potential. Term insurance is a basic "no frills" form of life insurance and is the best value for most consumers. You need coverage most while you are raising young children. Another nice feature of having a simple term life insurance policy is that you do not need to purchase the expensive credit life insurance for individual debts. The proceeds from the term policy can be used to liquidate all your debts.

People frequently ask about long-term care (LTC) insurance, since it is advertised a lot these days. Here is the conventional wisdom about this type of insurance. Many financial advisors do not recommend purchasing long-term care insurance. They note that odds are you will not need it or could make better arrangements for such care. Statistics say that 86% of men and 69% of women never need long-term-care, and there is only a 4% chance that those who do require long-term care will need to remain in a nursing home for longer than five years. Instead they recommend self-insurance. Put $3,000 each year—a typical LTC premium for a person in his 50s—into an emergency fund, or use this money to pay off the mortgage on your home faster.

If you own your house free and clear, when you have to go into a nursing home at age 85, you can sell the house and use the proceeds to help pay for the cost of long-term care.

Variable Expenses

Planning for variable expenses is not as easy as budgeting for savings or fixed expenses. Variable expenses will fluctuate by household situation, time of year, health, economic conditions, and a variety of other factors. A good guide to these items is to compare what you spent on these items over the past year.

The most common overspending areas are entertainment and food, especially away-from-home meals. Purchasing less expensive brand items, buying quality used products, and avoiding credit card purchases are common budget adjustment techniques.

Developing a Successful Budget

Having a spending plan will help to eliminate many financial worries, but a budget will work only if you follow it. Changes in income, expenses, and goals will require changes in your spending plan. Money management experts advise that a successful budget should be:

- *Well planned.* A good budget takes time and effort to prepare. The one we have included with this lesson is simple, yet comprehensive, and can be adapted to almost any income and expense level, because it is based on percentages instead of dollar amounts. Planning a budget should involve everyone who is affected by it. Children can learn important money management lessons by helping to develop and use the family budget.
- *Realistic.* If you have a moderate income, do not expect to save enough money immediately for an expensive car or an expensive vacation. A budget is not designed to prevent you from enjoying life but to help you achieve what you want most.
- *Flexible.* Unexpected expenses and changes in your cost of living will require a budget that you can easily revise. Also, special situations, such as two-income families or the arrival of a baby, may require an increase in certain types of expenses.
- *Clearly communicated.* Unless you and others involved are aware of the spending plan, it will not work. The budget should be written and available to all household members. Many variations of written budgets are available. You can start by using the one included with this lesson. There are many good computerized spending plans as well. Just be sure to include your tithe and offerings as the first items to access God's promised wisdom and blessing in managing your financial stewardship.

The Bible encourages savings and storing up for the future. But saving is the most difficult budget item for most families. To save on a consistent basis, most people need to override human nature. How can this be done? The best way for many of us is to put savings on autopilot. Arrange for a certain percentage of each paycheck to be tucked away. This takes little discipline or effort. Many employees have automatic payroll-deduction plans available for savings and retirement accounts. You can also arrange for your bank or mutual fund firm to take money out of your bank account every month. (A simple payroll deduction each pay period to our credit union savings account allows us to have the money each year for our income and property taxes when they are due.)

It will take a little time for your family to set up its budget initially, but after a while, you will find that it is easy to maintain, and soon you will see financial freedom that will bring great satisfaction in this area of your life. Remember to make several copies of the budget/spending plan form and begin early this week to develop your own personal budget. If you have children in private school, use the budget line for "Books and continuing education" for your tuition and fees. It is likely that you will need to increase the percentage in this column. What that means is that you will have to take away from some other area. Many families live very prudently during the time of their children's education.

Pray that God will guide you as you develop your budget that puts Him first. He is your Partner in this process. Keep your budget and balance sheet in your file for easy reference.

Assignment for this lesson:

1. Memorize Psalms 1:1-3.
2. Complete the worksheets for this lesson.
3. Complete the "Spending Plan" budget included with this lesson—Form #5.
4. Continue to pray for God's wisdom and blessing as you study these lessons.

Developing a Spending Plan

Memory Text: Psalms 1:1-3

"Blessed is the man who walks not in the counsel of the ungodly, nor stands in the path of sinners, nor sits in the seat of the scornful; But his delight is in the law of the LORD, and in His law he meditates day and night. He shall be like a tree planted by the rivers of water, that brings forth its fruit in its season, whose leaf also shall not wither; and whatever he does shall prosper."

PRAYER TIME:

Make a list of those in your group who have asked for special prayer needs this week and pray for them each day.

_____

_____

Pray also for God's wisdom and blessing as you develop your financial plan.

STUDY TIME:

Day One

Read and reflect on Proverbs 27:23-24 and Luke 14:28-30.

1. What are the budget implications from these passages? _____

_____

_____

_____

2. What role does estimating and planning play in developing your budget? _____

_____

3. Do the first (rough draft) of the spending plan (Form #5).

   (Make several copies of the form before you get started so that you can keep refining it.)

Day Two

Read and reflect on Proverbs 3:5-10 and Matthew 6:31-33.

1. According to these verses, where should God fit into our budgeting process? _____

_____

_____

_____

2. Why do you think God asks us to put Him and spiritual things in that position? _____

_____

_____

_____

3. What are some of the promises God makes to those who follow His counsel in their financial priorities?

_____

_____

_____

4. Continue to refine your spending plan with Form #5.

Day Three

Read and reflect on 1 Timothy 5:8.

1. Can a person adequately provide for his family without a spending plan? _____

_____

_____

2. Would savings and planning for the future be included in this text? Explain. _____

_____

_____

_____

3. How could a simple term life insurance policy contribute to providing for a family's basic needs? Explain.

_____

_____

_____

4. Why did Ellen White discourage the purchase of life insurance in the period between 1867 and 1906?

_____

_____

_____

Day Four

Read and reflect on Matthew 22:21.

1. What do you think Jesus meant when He said, "Render to Caesar the things that are Caesar's"? _____

_____

_____

_____

2. Are personal income taxes part of what we owe Caesar? Why? _____

_____

_____

_____

3. What can a family do to legally minimize income taxes? _____

_____

_____

_____

_____

Read and reflect on 1 Corinthians 16:1, 2 and Acts 20:35.

4. What do these verses teach us about the place of giving in the Christian's budget? _____

_____

_____

_____

How can it really be more blessed to give than to receive? _____

_____

_____

_____

_____

Day Five

Complete your spending plan—Form #5—today.

Then do the exercise of comparing the suggested percentage amount in the first column based on your income and the actual amount that you are spending in each category in column three. Then note the difference in the fourth column. This will allow you to see areas where you are spending more than the suggest percentage. **Remember, this is not just a "busy work" project, but it is a very beneficial tool for you to see and plan for your spending habits.**

Day Six

As your time allows, read and reflect on Genesis chapter 41.

1. What was meant by the seven fat cows and the seven gaunt cows in the king's dream? _____

_____

_____

_____

_____

_____

2. What does this passage suggest about the value of having an emergency savings fund? _____

_____

_____

_____

_____

_____

Monthly budget/Spending Plan

Note: Percentages are suggested as a point of beginning and may be adjusted as needed except for tithe and taxes.

INCOME (Monthly)	BUDGETED AMOUNTS		ACTUAL AMOUNTS	VARIANCE
	Dollar	Percent		
Salary (gross)				
Other income				
Total income		**100%**		
Expenses (set aside and savings)				
Tithe		10		
Offerings		5		
Taxes: Fed, State, FICA		21		
Emergency fund savings		2		
Savings for vacation		2		
Savings for investment		2		
Total set aside and savings		**42**		
Fixed Expenses				
Mortgage or rent		18		
Property taxes		4		
Auto loan/auto savings		5		
Life insurance (term)		1		
Total Fixed Expenses		**28**		
Variable Expenses				
Food		9		
Utilities: phone, heat, electric, water		5		
Clothing		3		
Transportation: auto operation, repairs, public transportation		7		
Personal and health care		2		
Entertainment		1		
Books and continuing education		1		
Gifts		1		
Personal allowance, misc.		1		
Total variable expenses		**30**		
Total (must be less than or equal to income)		**100%**		

Note: *Once you have established your monthly income, you can simply multiply that total by the percentage in each column to put your target budget amount in the first column. Once you have done that step, then you can put the actual amount you are spending in column three for comparison. You can then easily see where you need to make adjustments. For example, if you are spending less than 9% of total income on food then you can transfer a percent or two from that column to where it is needed elsewhere. But remember you only have 100% to spend!*

Lesson 6

Training Children, Money and Marriage, Money and Singles

Memory Text: Philippians 4:11-13

"Not that I speak in regard to need, for I have learned in whatever state I am, to be content: I know how to be abased, and I know how to abound. Everywhere and in all things I have learned both to be full and to be hungry, both to abound and to suffer need. I can do all things through Christ who strengthens me."

It is in the family relationship that stewardship is taught and caught. Unfortunately, many families are out to sea when it comes to money management, and consequently, so become many of the children. It has been possible to go through elementary school, high school, and even college and never have been required to take a course that gave good practical counsel on how to manage money or the best way to buy a car, a house, or an insurance policy. Fortunately that is changing. In fact, there are many good books available now, even from a Christian perspective like this one, that have good practical counsel on money management. In fact there is even a great deal of information on the Internet that can guide one in terms of managing, saving, and investing.

From a Biblical perspective, a family is a man and woman who have married and left their parents and established a new home together. This is apparently God's ideal living arrangement. Though we have tried to write this book with God's ideal principles espoused, we must all recognize that we do not live in an ideal world. It is in quite a mess due to the fall of man! By the grace of God, however, we must all strive for the ideal so that we can acknowledge God's wisdom and receive His blessings.

Singles also are recognized households in God's word. In fact, it is clear that many religious leaders in both the Old and New Testaments were single. From a financial perspective, singles have a greater challenge because of the likelihood of a smaller income stream in the same challenging financial environment as the married couple.

Who Should Manage the Money?

In our money management counseling over the years, we hear from couples who are married but maintain separate checking, saving, and/or spending accounts. They have "his money" and "her money." We have found, and also believe, it is Biblically true that when a couple gets married they "become one." This should include the management of the money in one account. "His money" and "her money" becomes "our money." We frequently mention in our finance seminars that before a couple gets married, they should inquire of the other's debt load, because, as a rule of thumb, when you get married you "inherit" the other's debts.

Who should control the money in a marriage? The man or the woman? The simple answer is both should work out the budget together, but the one who is the most talented or willing should be the one to be the manager. Families who manage with the least stress report that they work together on decision-making and have certain guidelines, like never spending over a certain amount—$100, for example— without consulting the spouse. If the couple works together on the balance sheet and the short and long-term goals, then they are more likely to work together on reaching those goals. We will talk later in the book about avoiding the trap of getting involved in get-rich-quick schemes. But it must be said here that whether or not your spouse knows anything about money management, God gave you that person to consult with and to keep you from doing stupid things. It is a time for real rejoicing when a debt is paid off or a needed item is purchased with cash.

Family Fundamentals

Sometimes we forget how sacred the family unit is. Jesus said, *"But from the beginning of the creation, God 'made them male and female. For this reason a man shall leave his father and mother and be joined to his wife, and the two shall become one flesh' so then they are no longer two, but one flesh. Therefore what God has joined together, let not man separate"* (Mark 10:6-9). This family unit is the very basis for society. *"Society is composed of families, and is what the heads of families make it. Out of the heart are 'the issues of life'; and the heart of the community, of the church, and of the nation is the household. The well-being of society, the success of the church, the prosperity of the nation, depend upon home influences"* (The Adventist Home, p. 15).

Proper money management and the stewardship of the resources God has given us in time, talent, (body) temple, and treasures is best taught in the home with other fundamentals such as work ethic, integrity, and faithfulness to duty. The value of family cannot be overstated. *"The family tie is the closest, the most tender and sacred, of any on earth. It was designed to be a blessing to mankind. And it is a blessing wherever the marriage covenant is entered into intelligently, in the fear of God, and with due consideration for its responsibilities"* (Ibid., p. 18). *"One well-ordered, well-disciplined family tells more in behalf of Christianity than all the sermons that can be preached"* (Ibid., p. 32).

Since we do not live in an ideal world, the basic family unit described above is not as common as it once was. Whatever circumstances you find yourself in, pray for God's guidance and do your best to follow the Biblical principles outlined in this book. You will be blessed in following God's plan. For example, in the budget area, if you are a single parent, you must still develop your budget by adding all sources of income and using that figure to take care of your expenses.

The rules governing life do not come by chance— they must be learned. Learning is easier during the early formative years of life when the mind and character are developing. So, the best time to learn and practice these principles is during childhood, and this indicates the importance of the home and its vital influence.

Guidelines for Training Children

The home environment is fundamental. Here the characters of the children are developed. The Bible says, *"Train up a child in the way he should go: and when he is old, he will not depart from it"* (Proverbs 22:6). Untold numbers of people, who are the products of well-disciplined, Christian homes, are a testimony to the truth of this statement.

When we study guiding principles for the family, we learn that the location of the home is very important. In reviewing the plight of Lot and his family, the counsel is given, *"When Lot entered Sodom he fully intended to keep himself free from iniquity and to command his household after him. But he signally failed. The corrupting influences about him had an effect upon his own faith, and his children's connection with the inhabitants of Sodom bound up his interest in a measure with theirs. The result is before us.*

"Many are still making a similar mistake. In selecting a home they look more to the temporal advantages they may gain than to the moral and social influences that will surround themselves and their families. They choose a beautiful and fertile country, or remove to some flourishing city, in the hope of securing greater prosperity; but their children are surrounded by temptation, and too often they form associations that are unfavorable to the development of piety and the formation of a right character …

"In choosing a home, God would have us consider, first of all, the moral and religious influences that will surround us and our families…Those who secure for their children worldly wealth and honor at the expense of their eternal interests, will find in the end that these advantages are a terrible loss. Like Lot, many see their children ruined, and barely save their own souls. Their lifework is lost; their life is a sad failure. Had they exercised true wisdom, their children might have had less of worldly prosperity, but they would have made sure of a title to the immortal inheritance" (Patriarchs and Prophets, pp. 168,169).

The ideal home environment is a simple one. The closer the family can live to nature, the better, for this will be a constant witness to God's creative power. All members of the family, both children and parents, benefit from less of the artificial, man-made environment. Most people would agree that the country is the best environment for the home. This was the model setting which God provided for humanity's first home. Among the flowers and trees, beside the singing brooks, humanity would find its greatest joy and contentment.

Lessons from a Garden

As a developer of character, a garden is one of the most important activities of the home. We realize that in the days of the small subdivision lot or the high-rise apartment, this seems rather strange. However, growing anything with the children involved—even a simple flower garden—can teach valuable lessons. The demonstration of human effort combined with divine power is easily portrayed. In no other activity can this principle be seen so graphically as in the planting and growing of plants. If there is room on your property for doing this outside, you have the added benefits of fresh air and exercise. Gardening also teaches responsibility. Children find great satisfaction in seeing vegetables and flowers that they have helped produce.

It is man's work to prepare the soil and plant the seed. But once the seed is in the ground, man is helpless until God brings it to life. Man can carefully tend the plant—weeding, hoeing, and watering—but it is God who provides the sunshine and the rain so essential to its growth.

As parents we must recognize that bringing children into this world is an awesome responsibility. How many children should a family have? In the last century families were large with four or more children in each household. It was felt that children were necessary to help with work around the home. In the post-modern culture, families are much smaller, and some couples choose not to have children at all. If there are children in the family, the Bible gives counsel that they should be instructed throughout the day. *"And these words which I command you today shall be in your heart. You shall teach them diligently to your children, and shall talk of them when you sit in your house, when you walk by the way, when you lie down, and when you rise up"* (Deuteronomy 6:6,7).

The best way to teach children to manage money is to let them use it. This can be done very early in their lives by giving them an allowance before they are old enough to work. Then they can figure their own tithe, offerings, savings, and spending money. The counsel we have in this area is very pointed and practical: *"Let every youth and every child be taught, not merely to solve imaginary problems, but to keep an accurate account of his own income and outgoes. Let him learn the right use of money by using it. Whether supplied by their parents [this would be an allowance] or by their own earnings, let boys and girls learn to select and purchase their own clothing, their books, and other necessities; and by keeping an account of their expenses, they will learn, as they could learn in no other way, the value and the use of money"* (Child Guidance, p. 136).

People always ask, "How old should our children be when we start teaching them about money management?" We have a simple answer. *"When very young, children should be educated to read, to write, to understand figures, to keep their own accounts. They may go forward, advancing step by step in this knowledge"* (Ibid.). When do we teach them the three Rs? Very early! Many children learn to count and read and write at five or six years of age! This counsel adds, "to keep their own accounts." Obviously, these young children would not be doing accounting, but they could be given little banks or jars in which they could put their tithe, offerings, savings, and spending money.

Many parents open checking accounts for their children when they are ten years old, so they can gain the experience of managing money under the supervision of their parents. As the counsel states above, once children learn to manage money, they can then begin to do their own purchasing of books, clothing, and other needs. What great value this is for kids!

Parents can model financial faithfulness in their own management, set the example of returning tithe and offerings at church, and teach stewardship in family worship. One of the best management principles that parents can model and teach is diligence in work. The Bible states, *"Do you see a man who excels in his work? He will stand before kings; He will not stand before unknown men"* (Proverbs 22:29). If a child is taught honesty, integrity, and a willingness to work, he can make his way in life and not be a burden on society.

Help For College Expenses

Because of the great value to the child and the significant expense to all concerned, plans should be made to provide for a college education. This can be done in a number of ways. Here are some of the best. To begin with, it should be instilled in the children that in order to be able to provide for their own needs and to serve others, an education is important. They should also understand that to get an education requires a plan that includes diligence, that is, hard work on their part, and money. Early on children should be taught the value of work and how to do it. Lessons of responsibility, promptness, and punctuality should be taught by story and example. This can be done by having the children assist you in work projects, giving them tasks to perform, and reading to them character building stories at bedtime and worship periods.

Parents and students should know that grants and scholarships are available for students who have shown promise in academy or high school by doing well academically, demonstrating leadership skills, and by becoming involved in extra-curricular activities—like involvement in the choir, tumbling team, band, orchestra, student government, yearbook and student newspaper. All Adventist colleges in North America offer scholarship rewards for such activities that result in discounts for tuition expenses. It should be noted here that if any one of the colleges offers a grant or scholarship to a student, most of the other colleges would match it if the student decides to attend one of them. These grants and scholarships can add up to a substantial discount on the college bill. All the student has to do is attend class, keep up his/her grades, and remain in good standing at the college!

The second important factor in paying for a college education is student initiative. There was a time when all students at college had jobs and worked faithfully at them to help defray the cost of their education. The academic dean even set up the class schedule to accommodate working students! For example, all upper division classes were taught in the morning so that third and fourth year students could work in the afternoon. Unfortunately, this does not seem to be the case in many schools today. But still there are many opportunities for students to work part-time to assist with their school expenses. A goal should be set—for example, $1,000 of the summer work income of the student should be saved for the following year's school expenses. Then when school starts, the students should plan to work at least fifteen hours per week with the bulk of the money earned, after tithe, offerings, and taxes, to go on the school bill. Most students, as adults, report that what they learned in job skills and work-related experiences were a real benefit to them later in life. (Our family members would vouch for the value of college jobs.)

The third factor in helping to defray college expenses is parental assistance. We believe that parents owe their children the benefit of a college education. The primary goal of parenting for life here on this earth is to prepare children to become independent adults—physically, mentally, and spiritually. In addition to a Christ-centered home life, Christian education is a basic necessity. Some parents may not be able to contribute all of the balance after the scholarship, grants, and student labor is applied; however, there should be a sacrificial effort made to assist as much as possible to help children cover the cost of their college education.

Many financial planners, and even the Wall Street Journal, have suggested to parents that the best college planning for their children would be to prepay their home mortgage while the children are young. Once the home is paid off, the family can use the money that was going for the mortgage payment to either save for college or pay for college when the children are in school. If planned for in advance, this would be a very good system. The parents can be in the secure position of home ownership, and the children can finish college debt-free.

Before discussing student loans, we want to emphasize another important factor to consider when addressing the topic of college education. The problem is that the majority of college graduates end up working in careers that have nothing to do with their college education. There are several reasons for this phenomenon. Maybe the student doesn't really enjoy the types of jobs that are available in his field of study. Or, maybe there are no jobs available to graduates of a certain major, etc.

In order to avoid these problems, students should take interest and aptitude tests while still in high school in order to discover their interests and aptitudes. We highly recommend Career Direct, which is available through Crown Ministries at www.crown.org. With the Career Direct materials, students take a series of tests on the computer that helps them to determine their aptitude—whether they are good at science/math or humanities, etc.—and their interests—whether they enjoy working alone or with a group of co-workers etc. They may have an interest in a health-related field. The tests will allow them to see if they are fitted for such a career and whether or not jobs likely will be available in that area when they finish school. Without such testing, a student or family could spend $60,000-$100,000 and four years of time on some major that has little or no economic value in the real world.

What About Student Loans?

We are frequently asked about the propriety of going into debt to get an education. Our answer is direct and simple. You should take out a student loan only after you have done everything else that has been recommended. Apply for all the grants and scholarships for which you qualify. You do not have to pay these back; therefore, no interest is accruing on them. Work all you can both during the summer and during the school year. Apply the contribution of your parents. If there is a shortfall after these measures, only then should you borrow the least amount you can—not all you qualify for! This borrowing assumes you are taking a course for which there is a job when you finish and the additional education will enhance your earning capability. It would be a real shame to be stuck with a student loan payback for a course of training that was of no benefit!

The reason that you borrow only the exact amount that you will need to pay the balance of your bill is that you have to pay it all back with interest over a period of time. We also recommend that student loans be paid back as quickly as possible—not stretched out over thirty years as some loans allow. There are some jobs—like nursing, for example—that have such a shortage of qualified workers, some employers will amortize part or all of your tuition expense if you will work for them for a specified period of time after graduation.

The Credit Card Dilemma

In America we are moving rapidly toward a cashless society. Already almost three-fourths of financial transactions are conducted electronically. Many families pay most of their bills on-line, and make most of their purchases with credit cards. The dilemma occurs with the misuse of credit cards. Credit card misuse with cash advances, splurge spending, carry-over balances, and spending over the credit limit is for many the greatest source of family debt with its resulting stress. Studies show that for those families filing for bankruptcy protection, almost all have considerable credit card debt.

The conventional wisdom for your best credit score is that you have only one or two credit cards that you keep for a long time and pay off every month. It is not recommended that a person have store credit cards, such as Sears, Macy's, etc. These cards encourage only more specific spending, compound your debt, and make it harder to keep track of purchases when there are multiple cards. In addition, it should be common knowledge that most "store brand" credit cards make more money on the interest they charge

their customers on their unpaid balances than they do on the profit margin on the sale of the original purchase. Choose your credit card, such as a Visa or MasterCard, by the benefits it offers you, not what benefit there is to the card issuer. Many families find that the use of a debit card works well for young people. It allows them to spend only to the limit of their bank accounts. The habit of frequently getting cash from an ATM is also discouraged, as frequently there are fees attached to such transactions. Also, it is hard to document the use of the funds thus advanced.

Credit cards are nice for convenience and safety, but their use must be managed carefully to avoid the problems that come with over-spending and debt. It also should be noted that studies show that even among families that pay off their credit card balance faithfully each month, those who use credit cards spend more money and make more purchases than those who operate on a cash basis. At the time we are writing this book, the figures have just been released that Americans currently are carrying a collective balance on their credit cards of over $900 billion, and many families are behind in their minimum payments.

On Being Content

One of the primary goals of spiritual regeneration is to transform mankind from being selfish to being loving. Always thinking of ourselves and wanting more are selfish traits that we must overcome to be more Christ-like. In Paul's list of signs of the last days, the first two items involve man's attitude toward money and possessions. *"But know this, that in the last days perilous times will come: For men will be lovers of themselves, lovers of money..."* (2 Timothy 3:1, 2). Selfishness and love of money are significant descriptions of men living in the last days. And how well these characteristics describe our day!

It is interesting to note that in this selfish, money-loving society, Paul counsels us to be content with what God has given us and not desire to be wealthy. *"Now godliness with contentment is great gain. For we brought nothing into this world, and it is certain we can carry nothing out. And having food and clothing, with these we shall be content. But those who desire to be rich fall into temptation and a snare, and into many foolish and harmful lusts which drown men in destruction and perdition. For the love of money is a root of all kinds of evil, for which some have strayed from the faith in their greediness, and pierced themselves through with many sorrows"* (1 Timothy 6:6-10).

So how much is enough? As a general rule most people in America spend whatever they make—no matter how much it is. Some even spend more than they make by going into debt. What is enough in clothing, food, electronic gadgets, television channels, sporting equipment, shoes, etc.? This is a very personal question, of course. No one else can answer it for us, but we answer it every day by the purchasing choices we make. We must ask God to help us to differentiate between our needs, wants, and desires.

Satan is at work in our world determined to help us answer that question according to his perspective. Regardless of our income, our lifestyle, our investment portfolio, or class, the enemy wants us to respond in unison with one voice and answer, "Just a little more."

Just like self-denial, which is the hardest sermon to preach and the most difficult to practice, contentment does not come "naturally." It must be learned and practiced. Paul gave the counsel above but stated that it was a lesson that he also had to learn: *"Not that I speak in regard to need, for I have learned in whatever state I am, to be content: I know how to be abased, and I know how to abound. Everywhere and in all things I have learned both to be full and to be hungry, both to abound and to suffer need. I can do all things through Christ who strengthens me"* (Philippians 4:11-13).

You can be a discontent millionaire or a discontent pauper. Discontentment knows no economic boundaries. The common denominator is a gnawing desire to have what is just out of reach or what someone else has, believing that it will make us—finally—truly happy. Discontentment dries our spirit. It does so, because, at its core, it is an indictment of God's gracious care and provision in our lives. It accuses

God of holding back and holding out. It assumes that we deserve more, but somehow we are not receiving all we really need.

Apparently, Solomon knew this tendency of mankind to be discontented. He prayed, *"Remove falsehood and lies far from me; Give me neither poverty nor riches—Feed me with the food allotted to me; Lest I be full and deny You, And say, 'Who is the Lord?' Or lest I be poor and steal, and profane the name of my God"* (Proverbs 30:8, 9). The presence, provision, and providence of God should bring peace and satisfaction to us all. Let's make a personal commitment to ourselves and to our families to be content in Christ.

What About our Homes

Where we live, the kind of house we live in, and how we maintain it tells a lot about us. The Bible is clear that God is building a home for us in heaven. Some versions describe it as a mansion. It certainly will be a mansion compared to anything we have seen on this earth! We are advised to have a single-family home, in the country, on high ground, with sufficient land for a garden, and paid off—no mortgage! What a big order! A Christian's home should be comfortable, but not extravagant. In the next chapter we will discuss major purchases, such as an automobile and a home. You will find some great tips for wisely making these larger purchases.

The home is the place where the family learns together to trust God to provide financially. The home is the place where counsel and example teach the children how to return their tithes and offerings to God. The home is the place where the children are taught responsibility in keeping their rooms clean and orderly and where the family works together to take care of family chores. The entire family can be involved in the purchase and preparation of food and the clean-up afterward.

The home is the place where the children can be taught to open a checking account, to balance the checkbook, and to keep a record of income and expenditures. Children can also be taught how to save for more expensive items. The home is the place where children can be taught the value of quality items that will last a long time and hold their value. The home is the place where the children can learn lessons of thrift and economy.

The Self-denial Box

We have been counseled, *"In every home there should be a self-denial box, and that into this box the children should be taught to put the pennies they would otherwise spend for candy and other unnecessary things. They are to be taught that there is a great work to be done for a needy, suffering people. . . . You will find that as the children place their pennies in these boxes, they will gain a great blessing. . . . Every member of the family, from the oldest to the youngest, should practise self-denial"* (*Review and Herald*, June 22, 1905). The self-denial box is mentioned many times, and a number of uses for the funds are given including the following:

- to lift the debt from the local church
- to support the missions of the church
- to keep the family out of debt
- to help the poor
- to help the family in an emergency

This self-denial box plan is one way for a family to demonstrate interest in and support of God's church and to plan ahead for unexpected expenses. The neat thing about it is that the entire family can work together in self-denial for the benefit of others.

In Summary

Every member of the family can be a part of the family finances by being a part of earning, giving, saving, and spending decisions. The husband and wife should each have a certain amount of money to use according to their own discretion. They should see themselves as partners in the family firm.

Children should have allowances so they may learn (under parental guidance) the use of money. First, they should be brought to recognize that all money belongs to God, and it is to be used by them wisely and sparingly. They should be taught to set apart the tithe and a freewill offering before any portion of their allowance is used for personal things. This can be done as soon as they are old enough to count to ten on their fingers.

One caution about allowances would be children need to understand the rules for "paying" and "non-paying" jobs. Some chores, like keeping your room clean and putting toys away, should be done simply because they are members of the family. This teaches teamwork, cooperation, and individual responsibility. Other tasks, like mowing the lawn or washing the family car, could be presented as paying opportunities. Children need to know about accountability, quality of work, and the concept of reward. The home and its duties provide an excellent venue for these types of teaching opportunities.

The world has every right to expect that those professing godliness shall carry their beliefs into their business. If even one member tends to greed, deception, or dishonesty in business, it has an adverse effect on the entire body.

Someone has said that in church we talk about religion; in business, we put it into practice. Children will learn business integrity by the example of their parents. Caution must be constantly exercised in so many things that, in and of themselves, seem insignificant. Little they may be, but the principle is the same as in big things. Jesus called attention to the importance of little things, by saying, *". . . because you were faithful in a very little, have authority over ten cities"* (Luke 19:17).

Assignment for this lesson:
1. Memorize Philippians 4:11-13.
2. Complete the worksheets for this lesson.
3. Pray for God's guidance as you organize your family finances.

Training Children, Money and Marriage, Money and Singles

Memory Text: Philippians 4:11-13

"Not that I speak in regard to need, for I have learned in whatever state I am, to be content: I know how to be abased, and I know how to abound. Everywhere and in all things I have learned both to be full and to be hungry, both to abound and to suffer need. I can do all things through Christ who strengthens me."

PRAYER TIME:

Make a list of those in your group who have asked for special prayer needs this week and pray for them each day.

_____

_____

Pray also for God's wisdom and blessing as you develop your financial plan.

STUDY TIME:

Day One

Read and reflect on Mark 10:6-9.

1. What principles could be drawn from this passage for family money management? _____

_____

_____

2. What kind of problems develop when only one spouse makes all the money decisions? _____

_____

_____

3. Isn't it really better when each spouse manages his own separate income? Explain your answer. _____

_____

_____

_____

_____

4. Under ideal circumstances, which spouse should be the family money manager? _____

_____

_____

5. Why does Ellen White call marriage a covenant? What does the word "covenant" mean? _____

_____

_____

_____

Day Two

Read and reflect on Proverbs 22:6.

1. Should our training of children include money management skills? Compare Proverbs 22:6 with verse 7.

2. Why is the location of the home so important for children? _____

_____

_____

3. Read the quotation from *Patriarchs and Prophets*, pp. 168, 169 (quoted in the lesson above). State

why you think Lot moved his family into Sodom. Did he accomplish his goals for his family?

_____

_____

_____

4. Lot entered Sodom a wealthy man and came out with nothing. What factors caused this condition?

_____

_____

_____

5. What points could we learn from the experience of Lot in Sodom? _____

_____

_____

Day Three

Read and reflect on Deuteronomy 6:1-7.

1. What were God's people commanded to teach their children? _____

_____

_____

2. Four times each day, God's people were to use for teaching their children. When are the four times?

_____

_____

3. What should children be taught about money management? What is the best way to teach them?

_____

_____

4. How old should children be when parents begin to teach them to handle money? _____

_____

_____

5. Should parents provide their children with an "allowance"? Why or why not? _____

_____

_____

Day Four

Read and reflect on Ephesians 6:1-4.

1. What do you think the impact of "obedient children" is on our society? _____

_____

_____

2. What does it mean to "provoke" a child? _____

_____

_____

3. In verse 4 fathers are encouraged to raise children "in the training and admonition of the Lord." In a practical sense, what does this mean? _____

_____

Read and reflect on 1 Peter 2:11-12.

4. What attitude should the believer have about his earthly life? Explain what impact this has on the way the believer would live. _____

_____

5. List some sinful desires that "war against the soul" and explain their impact on individual spirituality.

_____

_____

6. What are examples of "good deeds" that would have in impact on others, according to verse 12?

_____

_____

Day Five

Reference "Help for College Expenses" in the lesson above.

1. How important is education in relation to financial success? _____

_____

_____

2. With college being so expensive, what four things can be done to help cover the costs?

_____

_____

3. What can parents encourage young people to do to avoid taking a major that has few jobs available or one the graduate would not enjoy? _____

_____

_____

4. When should student loans be considered, and why should students only borrow the very minimum they need? _____

_____

_____

Day Six

Read and reflect on 1 Timothy 6:6-10.

1. What does it mean to be content with what we have? Should we not strive to better ourselves?

   _____

   _____

2. What are the problems those who desire to be rich encounter? Name as many as you see in this passage. _____

   _____

   _____

3. How much is enough based on this passage? _____

   _____

   _____

Read and reflect on Proverbs 30:8, 9.

4. Why does the author of this passage pray that God would give him neither poverty nor riches?

   _____

   _____

5. Pray that God will bless you with just enough to keep you focused on your eternal reward.

   _____

   _____

Read and reflect on Matthew 5:13-16.

6. What is meant by "salt" in this verse? Comment. _____

   _____

   _____

   _____

7. How can a family be an effective witness to unbelievers with their money management? Could it be a part of the light that would shine from a family? _____

   _____

   _____

   _____

Lesson 7

Making Major Purchases

Memory Text: Luke 14:28

"For which of you, intending to build a tower, does not sit down first and count the cost, whether he has enough to finish it"

Every person making personal financial decisions is a consumer. Regardless of age, income, or household situation, we all use goods and services. Daily buying decisions involve a trade-off between current spending and saving for the future. While some people might shop for recreation and others only when necessary, both groups use techniques to get the most for their money. Wise buying decisions contribute to both our current personal satisfaction and our long-term financial security.

In very simple terms, the only way we can have long-term financial security is to not spend all of our current income. Overspending leads to misuse of credit and financial difficulties. A financial plan that includes good purchasing strategies will allow us to live within our means and prepare for the future. All major purchases require a strategy that seeks quality and economy in the same transaction. This strategy is frequently overlooked or bypassed when impulse buying is practiced. To avoid this trap, follow the practice of discussing with the spouse any purchase over $100. (This has worked well for us and could save you from making many unnecessary, even foolish purchases.)

In this chapter we will review the factors considered and recommended by financial planners and savvy purchasers, along with lessons we have learned through the years in making such decisions.

Transportation Decisions

Car ownership and operation is one of the major expenses in the budget. Most people spend more of their income on transportation than any other item except housing and food. For many households, expenditures on an automobile also exceed the amount spent on food when insurance, license fees, and road taxes are included. In addition there are the costs of gas, oil, maintenance, and repair. Over a period of fifty years, you can expect to spend over $200,000 on automobile costs, more than seven times the amount an average person spends on education.

With the cost of cars what they are today it certainly is a good idea to purchase wisely. In this section we will address automobile purchasing and/or leasing for the best benefit to your budget. Remember, you want quality and economy in the same transaction.

New or Used?

It is our conviction that under certain circumstances it is better to buy new than used. The reasons are simple. It is not simply the new car smell and the pride of ownership. In some cases, it makes good business sense. A sales person at a dealership that sold Hummers shared that a certain model sells new for over $70,000. However, in just one year, it would sell as a used vehicle for about $35,000—half the price in one year! This is a good example of buying just for smell and pride.

On the other hand, with some skill and negotiation one can purchase a new car for less than a comparably equipped 2-year old used car on the same dealer's lot. Timing and negotiating are important when purchasing a new car. In our area right now, competition to sell new cars has the prices so low (relatively speaking) that dealers make very little on the sale of a new car. They make their money on the sale of used cars that are traded in and on the service fees they charge their new car customers for maintenance and repair.

Dealers must sell certain quotas of cars each month and each year in order to be able to maintain their business and ordering status from the manufacturer. So, always at the end of the month, and particularly at the end of the year, they are ready to discount the sale price. In some areas, during the week between Christmas and New Year's Day, new car prices, including the "next year's models," sell for $5,000 to $12,000 off the regular price. The deals are better during this week because most families are thinking of Christmas expenses and holiday time with family rather than purchasing a car, so auto sales tend to be slow. Time your purchase to take advantage of this type of discount. Let the dealer pay for the first year or two's depreciation. This is the primary reason people purchase a used car—to save the first two years' depreciation.

Another point to consider is that when purchasing a new car you get the full manufacturer's warranty with the car and not just what is left, if any, on a used one. In addition, remember that every used car is for sale for some reason. It could be a reason that has nothing to do with the quality of the car. For example, it could be for sale because the original owner has passed away, is being transferred overseas, or is need of money. However, a significant number of used cars are for sale because the owner is having some problem with the car, it has been in an accident (the owner no longer has an emotional tie with it), or it just does not get good enough mileage, etc. If you buy a used car, try to determine why it is for sale.

If you like to trade cars often, then buying late model used cars is likely your best bet. You do not pay so much depreciation. If you keep your cars a long time—10 to 12 years or more—then you may wish to time your purchase for the best new car price. You can be the one to keep it maintained properly, to know its full history, and be entitled to the full manufacturer's warranty.

Buying a Used Car

The average used car in the United States sells for about $10,000. Americans spend over $100 billion a year to purchase more than twenty million used cars. So, even buying a used car should be done with due consideration to the expense. There are several sources for used car purchase. New-car dealers also sell used cars. Their supply of used cars is usually ones that they have taken in as trade-ins for new vehicles. New-car dealers generally give you a better warranty than other sellers because they have service departments and generally have lower mileage cars.

Used-car dealers get their cars from dealers and auto auctions and generally offer cars that are older and have higher mileage. Be aware that some used-car dealers obtain vehicles that have been poorly maintained.

Also private parties—individuals—sell their own used cars. Private party vehicles can be a bargain if they have been well maintained. They also can be a nightmare with no warranty. Some vehicles advertised in the paper appear to be for sale by the owner when in actual fact, the seller has just purchased a car from a dealer and is trying to re-sell it at a profit. Some sellers are trying to sell a car for a "friend" and have no idea of the car's true condition. Always ask for the owner's manual and the car's maintenance and repairs records.

Most used cars, even at new-car dealerships, are sold "as is," and the seller assumes no responsibility for any needed repairs—regardless of any oral claims by the seller. If a warranty is mentioned, get it in writing!

The appearance of a used car can be deceptive. A rusty body may have a well-maintained engine inside; a clean, shiny exterior may conceal major mechanical problems. You can avoid unwanted surprises later by getting the car inspected. Have a trained and trusted mechanic of your choice check the car out to estimate its present condition and to determine the cost of needed repairs.

To know whether or not you are "getting a good deal" on your car purchase, there are several places you should check before buying the car. You can find the price of similar cars in the newspaper, on car lots, and on the Internet at places such as Edmund's Used Car Prices. A number of factors influence the price of a used car: its mileage, features, options, and age.

The actual purchase money should come from your "transportation" savings account, possibly supplemented by your checking account or a loan from a bank or credit union. You probably will get better terms if you arrange your own financing rather than use what the dealer offers.

Buying a New Car

With budgetary factors in mind, the decision to buy a new car should never be based on impulse or emotional need. It should be based on your transportation needs and your financial readiness. As discussed earlier, it always is best to "time" your purchase, if possible, at the time when the dealerships are offering their best deals. Gathering information on the type of car you want from sources such as Consumer Reports and Edmunds will help you select a model that requires low maintenance, has good value retention, and will get good fuel economy.

Once you determine which model car you want to purchase, you can check out the options available for that model on the Internet and even determine a ball-park estimate of the price you can expect to pay. An important source of new-car price information is the sticker price. This is a printed form (usually posted on the side window of the vehicle) with its suggested retail price. This information label presents the base price of the car as well as the costs of accessories and other items. The dealer's actual cost, or invoice price, is an amount less than the sticker price. The difference between the sticker price and the dealer's cost is the range available for negotiation.

In this era of Internet information availability, you can find information about the dealer's cost from several sources. Edmund's New Car Prices and Consumer Reports are two such sources. You can find such information also in libraries and bookstores. You can use the dealer cost information to negotiate a deal that is only a couple hundred dollars above cost. Remember that to prevent confusion in determining the true price of the car that is being offered by the dealer, do not mention a trade-in vehicle until the cost of the new car has been settled. Then ask how much the dealer is willing to pay for your old car. If the offer price is not acceptable to you, sell the old car on your own.

If you do not feel comfortable negotiating the sale price on your own (it is kind of an uneven bargaining field, since the car salesperson does this everyday and has many tricks up his sleeve, while you only do this once every several years), you can engage the services of a buying agent such as that offered by AAA.

Paying for Your Next Car

Since you want to avoid debt, especially long-term debt, the best way to come up with the purchase money is to take it from your savings—your "transportation" savings account. If you presently do not have enough in that part of your budget/spending plan, then you will need to borrow the balance. Generally it is to your advantage to take any rebates the car dealer offers you and get your own financing instead of taking his "low rate" and getting no rebate. Under ideal circumstances, when your car loan is paid off, you should put an amount equal to the monthly payment into your transportation savings account each month so that you can pay cash when it is time to replace the vehicle.

Whether you buy a new or used car, it always is to your long-term advantage to service and maintain your car according to the owner's manual. It will serve you better and longer and also will be worth more when you are ready to trade or sell it. In fact, Consumer Reports has found that "If you keep your car going for 200,000 miles and 15 years, you may save as much as what the car originally cost you. By buying a reliable car, performing scheduled maintenance and fixing problems, an owner will save many thousands of dollars, compared with buying and financing the same model every five years. Example: The Honda Civic EX with automatic transmission could save its owner $20,500 if properly maintained for 15 years. That is about $1,500 more than the current purchase price." These are important points to aid in your financial planning.

What About Leasing a Car?

More than one-fourth of all new motor vehicles are leased. Leasing is a contractual agreement with monthly payments for the use of an automobile over a set period of time, typically three, four, or five years. At the end of the lease term, the vehicle usually is returned to the leasing company. Conventional wisdom says that leasing is not a good option for the average consumer for the following reasons: though you may have a lot of money "invested" in the car over the period of the lease, you have no ownership interest in the vehicle; you have to meet requirements similar to those qualifying for credit; and, in addition, you may have additional costs—for extra mileage (driving the car for more miles than the lease allowed), certain repairs, turning the car in early, or even a move to another state.

Generally, leasing would only make sense in a business use of a vehicle where the expenses could be written off as a business expense.

The Housing Decision

Unlike an automobile, shelter (a house) is one of man's basic needs. It generally is the largest budget expense item. Following good counsel in this area can mean the difference between "losing your shirt" and "making a profit." Houses cost a bundle. In fact, in many metro areas, housing prices have shot up so

fast that a large portion of families cannot afford to purchase. As a general rule, the reason houses cost so much is because credit is available. If there were no mortgage loans available, for how much would the average house sell? Not what they are selling for today by a long shot! But we have to live with the conditions that we face.

To Rent or To Buy

About 35% of U. S. households live in rental units. An apartment is the most common type of rental housing. For those who need more room, renting a house is also an option—though usually more costly than an apartment. There are three main advantages to renting. First is mobility. You do not have to go through the hassle of selling a house when you need to move; therefore, renting may be a good option if you are just going to live in an area for a short time—a year or two. The second advantage of renting is that there are fewer responsibilities. The owner takes care of the maintenance, property taxes, and casualty insurance. Finally, when renting (leasing), there are lower initial costs for getting into the house or apartment. Usually instead of a large down payment and closing costs that are associated with buying, the renter simply has to prepay a month's rent plus a security deposit (typically also equivalent to a month's rent).

With these considerations in mind, renting is likely the best option for those who are seeking temporary housing, who do not want the responsibility of home ownership, and who do not have sufficient savings to make a down payment on a house.

However, the disadvantages of renting suggest that renting is not the best long-term housing option. Renters do not enjoy the financial advantages homeowners do. Tenants cannot take tax deductions for mortgage interest and property taxes or benefit from the equity they build up in their homes. If you rent your entire working career and have no savings to purchase a home for retirement, then during this period of your life you must still continue to pay rent for someone else's property. Renters also are subject to rent increases over which they have little control. Tenants may be restricted regarding ownership of pets, personalization of the property, and acceptable levels of noise.

Should you decide to purchase a home, there are several options. A single-family dwelling, a multi-unit dwelling (such as a duplex or townhouse), a condo, cooperative housing, a manufactured home, a mobile home, and new home construction are the most common options. From our experience and general knowledge, a single-family dwelling is likely the best option with a mobile home lowest on the list. As a general rule, mobile homes are problematic. They may lose value over time; they may be difficult to sell in the future; they may be difficult to finance; and, construction quality may be poor.

When looking for a home to purchase, remember that our mansion is being built in heaven. We will have to leave all behind some day in the future and everything on this earth will get burned up: *"But the day of the Lord will come as a thief in the night, in which the heavens will pass away with a great noise, and the elements will melt with fervent heat; both the earth and the works that are in it will be burned up"* (2 Peter 3:10). You may not get all the features you want in your first home, but financial advisors suggest that you get into the housing market by purchasing what you can afford. As you move up in the housing market, your second or third home can include more of the features you want. There is much we could say about home buying, such as finding the home, having an inspection done, negotiating the price, etc. However, we will focus in the limited space in this chapter on paying the house off. You can get help with the other home buying tips online or in books at the library.

You are ready to buy a home when several factors are in place: you have all debts either paid off or under control; you have a 20% down payment saved up (in order to eliminate private mortgage insurance); and, you can afford the monthly payments including taxes and insurance. It would be well to note that it is generally recommended that your monthly housing payment should not be more than about 35% of you gross monthly income.

Paying Off Your Home Mortgage

Because of the severely inflated home prices that most potential home purchasers face, they have few options but to get a traditional home mortgage for either fifteen or thirty years (in order to qualify for the loan). Then, as able, they should accelerate payment of the mortgage by prepaying principle. There are several ways to do this. We will try to illustrate each one so that it will be easy to understand and follow.

Avoid or Eliminate Private Mortgage Insurance

Private mortgage insurance (PMI) is not your "homeowner's policy" that covers your home and its contents. PMI is an insurance that protects lenders from foreclosure loss due to their risk of making home loans that exceed 80% of the home's market value. PMI allows lenders to give loans to potential homeowners who have little or no cash saved up for a down payment. (Loans have been made when the purchaser has no down payment or as little as 5% or 10% cash down payments.) Borrowers should note that PMI is private insurance that can be canceled under certain circumstances. High-risk FHA lenders are protected by MMI (mutual mortgage insurance), and such policies can only be canceled by paying off the mortgage!

The reason you want to avoid or eliminate PMI is that it is a monthly premium that the purchaser pays that is roughly equivalent to an additional 1% is added to the mortgage interest rate. If your PMI monthly payment is $100, then if you avoided or eliminated it, you could add that $100 to the principal portion of your monthly payment and thereby pay off your home several years earlier. Also the PMI portion of your monthly payment is not tax deductible.

How to Avoid PMI

The simplest way to avoid PMI is to have a 20% down payment. Then it never becomes an issue or a payment. The next best way is not pretty. You must pay or prepay over 13 years' worth of mortgage payments (or 20% of the mortgage) to qualify for cancellation of the PMI. You must have been timely in your payments and have a loan that was obtained on or after July 29, 1999, for your PMI to be automatically canceled. You should be notified of such. A federal law, the Homeowner's Protection Act (HPA) of 1998, requires lenders to do this. If your loan pre-dates this law, then you must request your lender to cancel the PMI when you get to the 20% payoff point. Avoiding or eliminating PMI from your mortgage payment as soon as possible should be a major financial goal for your family. Then you can use the money you were spending for this insurance to prepay on your principal balance.

Paying Your Home Mortgage Early

By prepaying your mortgage principal, you can pay your house off years earlier than your amortization schedule shows. The first thing to note: make sure when you obtain a mortgage; there is no prepayment penalty. It should be written so in your closing documents, not just the oral statement of a closing agent.

Some individuals question whether or not the home mortgage should be prepaid. They feel that they will lose the tax advantage of the mortgage payment. But be aware that if you are in the 25% tax bracket, for every $1,000 you pay in home mortgage interest, you save $250 in taxes. This means simply that you have to spend a dollar to save a quarter—not a good deal! From our perspective, a family is wise to prepay its mortgage to get in a more secure position and to be ready to pay for college education and make investment goals.

For sake of illustration, we will use a $200,000 mortgage that is 80% of a $250,000 home. This is about the average home price in America today. The payment schedule or amortization schedule printed below will help you understand how to prepay your mortgage.

The preceding table shows only the first two years of a thirty-year loan. The constant is in Column

AMORTIZATION SCHEDULE

Loan Amount (Principal): $200,000   % Rate: 7.50   Years: 30   Monthly Payment: $1,398.43

	Payment #	Payment Amount	Interest	Principal	Principal Balance
1st YEAR	1	1,398.43	1,250.00	148.43	199,851.57
	2	1,398.43	1,249.07	149.36	199,702.21
	3	1,398.43	1,248.14	150.29	199,551.92
	4	1,398.43	1,247.20	151.23	199,400.69
	5	1,398.43	1,246.25	152.18	199,248.51
	6	1,398.43	1,245.30	153.13	199,095.38
	7	1,398.43	1,244.35	154.08	198,941.30
	8	1,398.43	1,243.38	155.05	198,786.25
	9	1,398.43	1,242.41	156.02	198,630.23
	10	1,398.43	1,241.44	156.99	198,473.24
	11	1,398.43	1,240.46	157.97	198,315.27
	12	1,398.43	1,239.47	158.96	198,156.31
	TOTALS	**16,781.16**	**14,937.48**	**1,843.67**	

	Payment #	Payment Amount	Interest	Principal	Principal Balance
2nd YEAR	13	1,398.43	1,238.48	159.95	197,996.36
	14	1,398.43	1,237.48	160.95	197,835.41
	15	1,398.43	1,236.47	161.96	197,673.45
	16	1,398.43	1,235.46	162.97	197,510.48
	17	1,398.43	1,234.44	163.99	197,346.49
	18	1,398.43	1,233.42	165.01	197,181.48
	19	1,398.43	1,232.38	166.05	197,015.43
	20	1,398.43	1,231.35	167.08	196,848.35
	21	1,398.43	1,230.30	168.13	196,680.22
	22	1,398.43	1,229.25	169.18	196,511.04
	23	1,398.43	1,228.19	170.24	196,340.80
	24	1,398.43	1,227.13	171.30	196,169.50
	TOTALS	**16,781.16**	**14,794.35**	**1,986.80**	

Number 2—the monthly payment of $1,398.43. Every month you must make at least one regular payment in order to pay the interest on the unpaid balance from the past month.

Now look at the amortization schedule and note the following: this payment schedule includes only the base payment of principal and interest. It does not include the amount that must be set aside in an escrow account to cover your property taxes, homeowner's insurance, and PMI if the loan amount is more than 80% of the value or sale price of the home. These additional expenses could add $200 or more to your monthly payment. But for purposes of showing prepayment of your mortgage, we will address only principal and interest.

One month after borrowing the $200,000, the first payment of $1,398.43 is due. Of this payment amount, $1,250.00 will go to the lender for interest; only $148.43 will go to "principal" to reduce the amount of the loan. Look at the first year total line. After paying $1,398.34 each month for an entire year, you have spent $16,781.16 on the loan repayment. Of this amount, $14,937.48 has gone to the lender as interest (profit), and you have reduced your loan by only $1,843.67! You still owe $198,156.31.

Now comes the joy of seeing how you can prepay principal payments and save thousands of dollars in interest that you never have to pay. (This is even more dramatic and visual than the "miracle" of compounding interest in your savings portfolio.) Let's illustrate. Let's say that when you make your first monthly payment that you have $300 dollars from some source—savings, income tax return, birthday gift, etc. If you would be willing to put this money toward paying off your mortgage, a dramatic result would occur. Look at the principal column for Payments Numbers 2 and 3. The amounts there are $149.36 and $150.29. Added together, they equal $299.65. You can take your $300 of discretionary money and make Payments Numbers 2 and 3 at the same time you make Payment Number 1. (Any time you make a regular payment, you can make as many additional payments as you want by simply prepaying the principal amount.)

So, when you make your Payment Number 1, simply enclose in the payment envelope a second check for $299.65 with a notation on the memo line of the check that this amount is for additional principal on your mortgage, Loan #_____. When you do this, there are two very good results. You have cut the length of your loan by two months, so your next payment is Number 4. But every bit as great is the fact that you saved the interest for Payments Numbers 2 and 3—that you never have to pay! That is by paying $299.65, you save $2,497.21, the combined interest for Payments 2 and 3. This is a return on your investment of 833%!

Let's illustrate another way. Suppose that during the month of December when you are preparing to make your twelfth payment, you also are thinking about putting $2,000 into your IRA. (Your IRA is currently earning 8%.) Then you think, "I wonder what would happen if I put this $2,000 on my home mortgage instead?" You check your amortization schedule and notice that if you were to make all of next year's payments (Numbers 13-24) in a timely manner, you will have paid $1,986.80 on your principal. You decide to use the $2,000 you were going to put in your 8% IRA on your home mortgage instead along with your December payment—Number 12. (Actually you should pay the exact amount of $1,986.80, so that you always know where you are in your amortization schedule.)

What would you accomplish by doing this? As you can easily see, you would make all twelve payments for Year Number 2 (Payments Numbers 13-24) and save yourself the entire year's interest of $14,794.35! Your next month's payment would be Number 25! There would be a return on your investment of 745%!

It turns out that your home mortgage is your very best investment in terms of guaranteed returns!

While it is true that the principal prepayment is easier and the benefits more dramatic in the early years of a mortgage, the $200,000 loan at 7.5% does not "break even" where the principal and interest are the same until Year Number 22 of payments. So, even twenty-two years into the mortgage, you still can make two payments at a time by paying the full monthly payment and half that amount for the second extra payment!

People frequently say, "The interest rate on my mortgage is only 6%, and I can get 10% or more in the stock market. Wouldn't it be better to invest my extra money in the stock market and pay off my home loan over the regular thirty-year amortization?" The answer to that question is that all money in the stock market is subject to loss in a bad economy. If your extra money is put in your house, it still will build up your net worth plus bring you closer to being totally debt free. Besides, where can you get 700%- 800% return on your investment with no risk?

Your goal is to become debt-free, including your home mortgage. You can achieve this goal by a planned prepayment strategy and the blessing of God. If you can approach the college education expense years with your home paid off, it will indeed be a blessing. In addition, as we will see later in the book, the major expense (about 35%) of the retirement budget of the majority of retirees is housing cost. If your home is paid off, you can live your retirement years with a 35% discount!

Finally, you must understand that this prepayment plan will work only as it should if you have no prepayment penalty associated with your mortgage and if you faithfully let your lender know in writing that you intend for the second check you are enclosing with your regular monthly payment to go on the principal of your loan. All the writing that is necessary is a notation on the memo line of your check: "Additional principal for Loan # _____; or, you simply can write the amount you are prepaying on the line designated on your payment coupon for "Extra Principal."

The Fifteen-Year Mortgage

Though the thirty-year mortgage is the most common in America, forty-year mortgages are also available under certain circumstances. However, taking out a fifteen-year mortgage may be the prudent route for those who can afford it. Obviously, a fifteen-year mortgage pays off in half the time of a thirty-year and saves a significant amount of interest to the purchaser. In addition, most fifteen-year mortgages are offered at a savings of 0.5% on the interest rate. So, if the current thirty-year fixed rate is 7.5%, you probably can get 7.0% on a fifteen-year mortgage.

Here is a comparison between a thirty and a fifteen-year mortgage on a $200,000 loan:

	Thirty years	Fifteen years
Monthly payment	$1,398.43	$1,797.66
Total interest paid	$303,434.45	$123,578.80

If you can afford $400 more on your house payment each month, you can pay the loan off in half the time and save yourself $179,855.65 in interest that you never have to pay!

As a general rule, we would not recommend a variable rate mortgage or an interest only mortgage. (We will address reverse mortgages in Lesson 9.)

Sub-prime Mortgages—Borrower Beware!

Just a generation ago, the average family simply could not get into the kind of financial hole that has become so familiar today. The reason was straightforward: a middle-class family could not borrow very much money. High-limit, all-purpose credit cards did not exist for those with average means. There were no mortgages available for 125% of the home's value. And there were no offers in the daily mail for second and third home equity loans.

As a result, a family that wanted to borrow money had only a handful of options. Instead of running up debt anonymously, a prospective borrower was forced to meet a stern-looking banker face-to-face. Families were asked to produce past tax returns, pay stubs, credit references, and projected budgets that showed how they planned to repay the money.

Then in 1975 Congress passed the "Equal Credit Opportunity Act." It stipulated, among other things, that lenders could no longer ignore a wife's income when judging whether a family earned enough to qualify for a mortgage. As a result, both families and banks had started down the path of counting Mom's income as an essential part of the monthly budget. This allowed families to qualify for more expensive houses and, at the same time, started the upward spiral of home prices.

A generation ago it was not possible to overload on a mortgage. It simply was not possible to give in to that temptation; mortgage lenders did not allow it! But today the game is different. It has become routine for lenders to issue unmanageable mortgages. The down-payment—once a critical device for screening potential borrowers—virtually disappeared in the banks' greed to draw more families into their interest making machine.

According to one study, families that make a down-payment of less than 5% of the purchase price of their home are fifteen to twenty times more likely to default than those who put 20% or more down.

A family with a sub-prime mortgage (over 80% of the home's value and a high interest rate) can end up paying twice as much for that home as a family that gets the market rate interest. Elizabeth Warren in her book, *The Two-Income Trap*, reports on p. 134 the following amazing scenario: "In 2001, when standard mortgage loans were in the 6.5 percent range, Citibank's average mortgage rate (which included both subprime and traditional mortgages) was 15:6 percent. To put that in perspective, a family buying a $175,000 home with a subprime loan at 15.6 percent would pay an extra $420,000 during the 30-year life of the mortgage—that is, over and above the payments due on a prime mortgage. Had the family gotten a traditional mortgage instead, they would have been able to put two kids through college, purchase half a dozen new cars, and put enough aside for a comfortable retirement."

Families seeking a mortgage for home purchase must be on guard against unscrupulous mortgage brokers. Many unsuspecting families are steered to an overpriced mortgage by a broker or some other middleman who represents himself as acting in the borrower's best interests, but who is actually taking big fees and commissions from sub-prime lenders.

During the sub-prime mortgage mess, banks were caught deliberately issuing mortgages to families that could not afford them with the ultimate aim of foreclosing on these homes. This practice was so common it had its own name in the industry—"Loan to Own." These lenders had found that foreclosing could be more profitable than simply collecting a mortgage payment every month. The property could be resold for more than the outstanding loan amount. So, the lender raked in fees at closing and high monthly payments for a few years, waited for the family to fall behind, and then swept in to take the property.

The lender won every possible way—high profits if the family managed to make all its payments, but even higher profits if the family did not.

The only way you can avoid being a victim of an unscrupulous lender is to borrow only if you can get a reasonable rate.

Closing Thoughts on Home Ownership

The late Christian financial counselor, Larry Burkett, stated, "It is my strong conviction that becoming debt-free, including the home mortgage, should be the first investment goal for any young couple (or person). Once you have achieved that goal, then, and only then, should you invest in other areas" (*Investing for the Future*, p. 142).

Ellen White gave similar counsel, *"Had Brother and Sister B been economical managers, denying themselves, they could ere this have had a home of their own and besides this have had means to draw upon in case of adversity"* (*Adventist Home*, p. 395). It is interesting to see that paying off the home and having an emergency fund are high priorities and reasonable goals for those who will live prudently.

She further counsels, *"We are not to feel disturbed if our neighbors build and furnish their houses in a manner that we are not authorized to follow"* (Ibid., p. 384). It may surprise some to realize that there are families not planning to go to heaven. Therefore, if they want a mansion, they must build it down here.

Making wise decisions on major purchases will be valuable for your long-range financial goals and allow you and your family to avoid many of the stresses that afflict the majority of families. As you complete the worksheets for this lesson, do so in a way that will bring you into conformity with God's will for you to be debt-free.

Assignment for this lesson:

1. Memorize Luke 14:28.
2. Complete the worksheets for this lesson.
3. Evaluate your housing situation and determine what, if anything, you could do now to save money and accelerate the payoff process.

Making Major Purchases

Memory Text: Luke 14:28

"For which of you, intending to build a tower, does not sit down first and count the cost, whether he has enough to finish it"

PRAYER TIME:

Make a list of those in your group who have asked for special prayer needs this week and pray for them each day.

_____

_____

Pray also for God's wisdom and blessing as you develop your financial plan.

STUDY TIME:

Day One

The area of major purchases for many families is one of those make or break financial decisions that impacts success or distress in our lives. Unfortunately, many make purchasing decisions with more attention to present desires than their long-term financial security. This lesson will give you practical suggestions that will allow you to purchase with confidence the items that you need.

1. Contemplate a purchasing decision you have made in the past that in retrospect was actually a bad decision. Why do you think it was bad? What would you do differently if you could make the decision again? _____

_____

_____

2. Recall a good purchasing experience from your past. What factors made this a good decision?

Note: *Remember that in these lessons, the whole point is that you learn information that will be valuable in your financial planning. You do not need to share any of your personal information, such as your balance sheet and budget with anyone, including the group leader. However, if you feel comfortable sharing the information you have noted above under 1 and 2, it might help others not to make the same mistake.*

Day Two

1. With respect to automobiles and transportation needs, what have you learned in this lesson that might be helpful in your next automobile purchase? _____

   _____

   _____

2. What are your family's transportation needs? (size of family, towing trailers, hauling things, commuting, all wheel drive, etc.) _____

   _____

3. Do you need more than one car? Explain why or why not. _____

   _____

4. What type of car(s) would satisfy your transportation needs? List several. _____

   _____

Days Three and Four

Fill out the following work sheet as an exercise to help you in your next purchase. It would be wise to photocopy this form so that you can fill out one for each car you would consider buying and then compare your research in order to make the best decision.

Auto Purchase Worksheet

Name of vehicle (Toyota Camry, Honda Accord, etc.) _____

Manufacturer's suggested retail price _____

Dealer invoice price _____

Incentives now available (rebates, discounts, financing, etc.) _____

_____

Three-year depreciation estimate _____

Repair history of this model _____

Rating by *Consumer Reports*? _____

Fuel economy rating _____

Cost of insurance for this model _____

Access to service in your area _____

Once you settle on the car you want, you are ready to compare the price at several dealers if you live in a metro area.

Day Five

Reference the material on housing—purchasing and renting—to answer the following questions.

1. What are the advantages of renting for housing needs? _____
_____
_____

2. What are the disadvantages of renting? _____
_____
_____

3. What are the advantages of owning your own home? _____
_____
_____

4. What are the disadvantages of owning? _____
_____
_____

5. What are the advantages of putting at least 20% down payment when purchasing a home with a loan?
_____
_____
_____

Who is the primary beneficiary of Private Mortgage Insurance? _____
_____
_____
_____

Day Six

Read the section in the lesson above on paying off your home mortgage early to answer these questions.

Note: *This section is not designed to encourage long-term indebtedness at this stage in earth's history. Rather it is included to help those who are already in a mortgage situation or for those who feel led to make a purchase to do so in a way that will limit the period of indebtedness.*

1. What is a pre-payment penalty? _____
_____

2. Is it better to pay off your mortgage or keep paying on it so that you can deduct your mortgage

    interest? Explain your answer. _____

    _____

    _____

3. If you currently have a home mortgage, dig out your amortization schedule (Order one

    from your loan company if you can't find it) and note your current principal, interest,

    and balance. After reading the mortgage prepayment material in this lesson, and

    reviewing your amortization schedule, what could you do to accelerate your payoff date?

    _____

    _____

    _____

    _____

4. Why would it be a bad idea to build a mansion here on earth? (See 2 Peter 3:10)

    _____

    _____

    _____

    _____

Lesson 8

Honesty, Integrity, Work

Memory Text: Colossians 3:23, 24

"And whatever you do, do it heartily, as to the Lord and not to men, knowing that from the Lord you will receive the reward of the inheritance; for you serve the Lord Christ."

Thus far we have covered many areas important to financial management. However, as significant as they are, it is not your balance sheet, your budget, your retirement plan, nor your estate plan that is the most important element of a successful family financial strategy. It is your character that manifests itself in your work habits, your dealings with others, and your interaction with family. In short, your work or vocation, your diligence, and your honesty and integrity will have more to do with your success in this life and your preparation for the life to come.

"No scheme of business or plan of life can be sound or complete that embraces only the brief years of this present life and makes no provision for the unending future" (*Education*, p. 145).

"That which lies at the foundation of business integrity and of true success is the recognition of God's ownership. The Creator of all things, He is the original proprietor. We are His stewards. All that we have is a trust from Him, to be used according to His direction.

"This is an obligation that rests upon every human being. It has to do with the whole sphere of human activity. Whether we recognize it or not, we are stewards, supplied from God with talents

and facilities, and placed in the world to do a work appointed by Him" (Ibid., p 137).

When we seek to find, understand, and practice the Biblical principles regarding life management, significant changes will occur in our lives. God has not promised that if we follow Him we all will become wealthy by the world's standards. But He has stated that if we will follow His statutes and revealed plan for our lives, we will be blessed. When Moses, the great leader of Israel, was about to lay down his life, he called all the people together on the plains of Moab and gave them three sermons. In essence, they are a review of God's faithfulness to them and an encouragement for them to be faithful to Him. In his third sermon, Moses outlines God's promised blessings for obedience (see Deuteronomy 28:1-14) and the promised curses for disobedience (see Deuteronomy 28:15-68). You can read the curses on your own. We want to share the awesome blessings that are promised to those who are obedient to God and follow Him.

Here are the promises: *"Now it shall come to pass, if you diligently obey the voice of the Lord your God, to observe carefully all His commandments which I command you today, that the Lord your God will set you high above all nations of the earth. And all these blessings shall come upon you and overtake you, because you obey the voice of the Lord your God:*

"Blessed shall you be in the city, and blessed shall you be in the country.

"Blessed shall be the fruit of your body, the produce of your ground and the increase of your herds, the increase of your cattle and the offspring of your flocks.

"Blessed shall be your basket and your kneading bowl.

"Blessed shall you be when you come in, and blessed shall you be when you go out.

"The Lord will cause your enemies who rise against you to be defeated before your face; they shall come out against you one way and flee before you seven ways.

"The Lord will command the blessing on you in your storehouses and in all to which you set your hand, and He will bless you in the land which the Lord your God is giving you.

"The Lord will establish you as a holy people to Himself, just as He has sworn to you, if you keep the commandments of the Lord your God and walk in His ways. Then all peoples of the earth shall see that you are called by the name of the Lord, and they shall be afraid of you. And the Lord will grant you plenty of goods, in the fruit of your body, in the increase of your livestock, and in the produce of your ground, in the land of which the Lord swore to your fathers to give you. *The Lord will open to you His good treasure, the heavens, to give the rain to your land in its season, and to bless all the work of your hand. You shall lend to many nations, but you shall not borrow.* And the Lord will make you the head and not the tail; you shall be above only, and not be beneath, if you heed the commandments of the Lord your God, which I command you today, and are careful to observe them. So you shall not turn aside from any of the words which I command you this day, to the right or the left, to go after other gods to serve them"* (Underlining by editor).

What family could afford to be without God's wisdom and blessing? This is one of the greatest treasure troves of promised blessings in the entire Bible! We take time to emphasize character and faithfulness in this chapter because real success in this world and preparation for the next are bound up in our partnership with God in the development of our characters. At the end of the day, this is all that really matters.

It is estimated that we spend between 95,000 to 100,000 hours of our lives working in gainful employment—our jobs or vocation. Strange as it may seem, many of us try to mentally separate our spiritual lives from our working lives. The fact is that our lives cannot be compartmentalized. When we work, play, read, worship, or engage in any of life's activities, we are living our lives. Life is not made up of a series of disconnected events but is the totality of those events.

As a Christian, every activity is an opportunity to glorify God. Whether we are working, playing, or resting, we are engaging in our Christian witness. From Gods' perspective our work and our witness merge. We are told, *"Not more surely is the place prepared for us in the heavenly mansions than is the special place designated on earth where we are to work for God"* (*Christ's Object Lessons*, p. 327). With this perspective in mind, we do not work simply to make a living. Our work is the place God wants us to be as His witnesses.

Many professional people are now looking at life in a far different way than they have in the past. Several witness while they work and share their means to help others and to advance the cause of God. Others add a third dimension. They manage their business affairs in such a way as to be able to be physically absent from their business at times and spend significant blocks of time—a month or more at a time—using their professional skills in overseas mission trips. Many are working directly in evangelistic outreach, and they report that they have never been happier!

More than Earning a Living

Because of the pressure to make ends meet, many times we think that our work is simply to provide an income. But as Christians we are faced with giving a response to the great commission that Jesus gave to his disciples. After quoting this command in Mark 16:15, Ellen White wrote, *"Not* that all are called to be ministers or missionaries in the ordinary sense of the term; but all may be workers with Him in giving the "glad tidings" to their fellow men. To all, great or small, learned or ignorant, old or young, the command is given.

"In view of this command, can we educate our sons and daughters for a life of respectable conventionality, a life professedly Christian, but lacking His self-sacrifice, a life on which the verdict of Him who is truth must be, "I know you not"?

"Those who reject the privilege of fellowship with Christ in service, reject the only training that imparts a fitness for participation with Him in His glory" (Education, p. 264).

How do we know whether or not we have found the place that God has designed for us to work on this earth and avoid the life of respectable conventionality mentioned above? We all know the basics. Get to know God by reading His word. Pray for God's guidance. Watch for His providential leading. We also are given a simple formula in the book Education: "We need to follow more closely God's plan of life. To do our best in the work that lies nearest, to commit our ways to God, and to watch for the indications of His providence-- these are rules that ensure safe guidance in the choice of an occupation" (p. 267).

In another very terse statement we are told, "To every man is given 'his work' (Mark 13:34), the work for which his capabilities adapt him, the work which will result in greatest good to himself and to his fellow men, and in greatest honor to God" (Ibid., p. 138).

These formulas might actually cause some to change professions so that they can be more in harmony with God's plan. Peter, Andrew, James, John, and Matthew did. In his Damascus road experience, Saul, who already had an education and a job, cried out to God, "Lord, what do you want me to do?" (Acts 9:6). He changed jobs and started a new career!

A Worker in the Church

We all cannot be pastors or full-time evangelists. But we must all respond to the great commission. We all can play some part in the support of God's church. The church was God's idea. He started it and gave gifts to it (see

Ephesians 4:8, 11). It is the unified church that, by the grace of God, takes the gospel to the entire world. No single individual, family, or person could ever hope to fulfill the commission alone. We all must understand the importance of church membership.

"Another obligation, too often lightly regarded—one that to the youth awakened to the claims of Christ needs to be made plain—is the obligation of church relationship.

"Very close and sacred is the relation between Christ and His church—He the bridegroom, and the church the bride; He the head, and the church the body. Connection with Christ, then, involves connection with His church.

"The church is organized for service; and in a life of service to Christ, connection with the church is one of the first steps. Loyalty to Christ demands the faithful performance of church duties" (Ibid., p. 268).

Work as God's Plan

Our Creator God placed Adam and Eve in an environment that allowed them the opportunity for work. "Then the Lord God took the man and put him in the garden of Eden to tend and keep it" (Genesis 2:15). In the process of creation, He established the weekly cycle and capped it off with the establishment of the Sabbath—a day of rest, refreshment, and fellowship with Himself. "Thus the heavens and the earth, and all the host of them, were finished. And on the seventh day God ended His work which He had done, and He rested on the seventh day from all His work which He had done. Then God blessed the seventh day and sanctified it, because in it He rested from all His work which God had created and made" (Genesis 2:1-3).

This work/rest cycle was so important for man's happiness that God also codified it in His written moral law given at Mt. Sinai. "Remember the Sabbath day, to keep it holy. Six days you shall labor and do all your work, but the seventh day is the Sabbath of the Lord your God. In it you shall do no work: you, nor your son, nor your daughter, nor your male servant, nor your female servant, nor your cattle, nor your stranger who is within your gates. For in six *days the Lord made the heavens and the earth, the sea, and all that is in them, and rested the seventh day. Therefore the Lord blessed the Sabbath day and hallowed it"* (Exodus 20:8-11).

It is very important to God that we remember this fourth commandment. It is a weekly reminder of our Creator God. Note how significant this fact is to God. He begins His codified word, *"In the beginning God created the heavens and the earth"* (Genesis 1:1). The Bible makes no attempt to prove the existence of God. It simply tells us that He created everything. By this statement we understand who God is—the Creator—and who we are—His creatures. He is the Owner. We are the managers. In Genesis, Chapter Two, we note that God made the seventh day holy as a reminder of His rest after creation and to set an example for us. The fourth commandment repeats this reasoning and codifies it in stone.

In the grand scheme of things, as we can see by a study of the prophecies, we understand that not only do we all individually have a life span or cycle of life, but so does the earth. God plans to renew everything back to its Edenic beauty and perfection: *"For behold, I create new heavens and a new earth; and the former shall not be remembered or come to mind"* (Isaiah 65:17). God's faithful followers have claimed this promise down through time—especially when we see the problems that sin has caused in the earth: *"Nevertheless we, according to His promise, look for new heavens and a new earth in which righteousness dwells"* (2 Peter 3:13).

As we near the end of this world's history, God gives Earth's inhabitants a final warning from an angel messenger: *"Then I saw another angel flying in the midst of heaven, having the everlasting gospel to preach to those who dwell on the earth—to every nation, tribe, tongue, and people—saying with a loud voice, 'Fear God and give glory to Him, for the hour of His judgment has come; and worship Him who made heaven and earth, the sea and springs of water'"* (Revelation 14:6, 7). This worldwide call includes a command to worship God as Creator of heaven and earth. In other words, God's last call to mankind is a call to honor the Creator—which we do by working and keeping the Sabbath holy.

It should be clear to all who seek God's plan for their lives that work through the week and rest on the Sabbath are included in man's part in receiving the covenant blessings of Deuteronomy 28:1-14. Remember, God said that if we would be diligent to obey and careful to observe His commandments that *"all these blessings will come upon you and overtake you"* (v. 2). When Adam and Eve were created, they had everything that they needed all around them. But God still wanted them to work for their own best good. Note these good reasons. *"Though rich in all that the Owner of the universe could supply, they were not to be idle. Useful occupation was appointed them as a blessing, to strengthen the body, to expand the mind, and to develop the character"* (*Education*, p. 21).

God feels that work is so important for our growth and development that He says, *"If anyone will not work, neither shall he eat"* (2 Thessalonians 3:10). Obviously, if a person is physically or mentally unable to work, this would not apply to them. However, for those who are able and choose not to work, there is a direct application.

The Rewards of Diligence

Solomon recorded, *"Do you see a man who excels in his work? He will stand before kings; He will not stand before unknown men"* (Proverbs 22:29). In many job environments today, the employers pay their employees just enough to keep them from quitting, and the employees work just hard enough to keep from getting fired. The Bible records several instances of employers who recognized that they were blessed because of having a godly employee. When Jacob desired to leave his father-in-law Laban and return with his family to his homeland, Laban entreated him not to leave: *"Please stay, if I have found favor in your eyes, for I have learned by experience that the Lord has blessed me for your sake"* (Genesis 30:27).

And when Joseph was sold into slavery in Egypt, his master Potiphar made a similar observation about Joseph's work and rewarded him accordingly: *"The Lord was with Joseph, and he was a successful man; and he was in the house of his master the Egyptian. And his master saw that the Lord was with him and that the Lord made all he did to prosper in his hand. So Joseph found favor in his sight, and served him. Then he made him overseer of his house, and all that he had he put under his authority"* (Genesis 39:2-4). How do our employers think about us? How do we treat our employees?

There is a Biblical model. Many of us have memorized this verse when we were younger: *"Therefore, whether you eat or drink, or whatever you do, do all to the glory of God"* (1 Corinthians 10:31). In our work and financial management and whatever we do, we should do it all to the glory of God. He is the one who gives us knowledge and strength to succeed in life. *"Yours, O Lord, is the greatness, the power and the glory, the victory and the majesty; for all that is in heaven and in earth is Yours; Yours is the kingdom, O Lord, and You are exalted as head over all. Both riches and honor come from You, and You reign over all. In Your hand is power and might; in Your hand it is to make great and to give strength to all"* (1 Chronicles 29:11, 12).

In order to have a balanced budget, there must be an income stream. It needs to be steady and consistent. Work is the means by which God provides our financial resources. Obviously, God could provide for our needs as He did for Israel during the forty years of wandering in the wilderness. But, for the many reasons we have discussed, God gives us the ability to work for our personal well-being.

Honesty and Integrity

The Bible says, *"A good name is to be chosen rather than great riches, loving favor rather than silver and gold"* (Proverbs 22:1). Our character is more important than the size of our bank account or our investment portfolio. It is unfortunate that many of the well-known "Christian ministries" in America have shown by the financial dealings of their leaders that they are not really Christian at all. In recent years, the U. S. Senate for obvious improprieties has investigated several of them.

When we tell someone what we will do with the money they entrust to us, we are duty bound before God to do just that. *"But let your 'Yes' be 'Yes,' and your 'No,' 'No,' lest you fall into judgment"* (James 5:12). There will never be an attempt to take advantage of someone or to cheat another in a transaction. God's people will always be fair and honest when they interact with others. *"You shall not have in your bag differing weights, a heavy and a light. You shall not have in your house differing measures, a large and a small. You shall have a perfect and just weight, a perfect and just measure, that your days may be lengthened in the land which the Lord your God is giving you. For all who do such things, all who behave unrighteously, are an abomination to the Lord your God"* (Deuteronomy 25:13-16).

Jesus is the embodiment of truth. And those who are genuine followers of His will be truthful always with whom they deal. *"Lying lips are an abomination to the Lord, but those who deal truthfully are His delight"* (Proverbs 12:22).

God calls Christians to a higher standard in work and life. The standard is God's law "written in our hearts" and reflected in our character. As society erodes and Christian teaching is diluted and minimized, it will become even more important for the individual Christian to live and work on a level that is above reproach. Daniel had such a reputation. When his political enemies tried to defame him, they had to acknowledge that he was a man of integrity. *"So the governors and satraps sought to find some charge against Daniel concerning the kingdom; but they could find no charge or fault, because he was faithful; nor was there any error or fault found in him"* (Daniel 6:4).

This is the attitude of the true steward: "Because of what Christ has done for me, I owe the world the best service I can give with the greatest gifts that I have—my life, my character, my self."

Biblical Principles of Management

The book of Proverbs is a reservoir of life management principles. *"Trust in the Lord with all your heart, and lean not on your own understanding; In all your ways acknowledge Him, and He shall direct your paths. Do not be wise in your own eyes; Fear the Lord and depart from evil. It will be health to your flesh, and strength to your bones. Honor the Lord with your possessions, and with the firstfruits of all your increase; So your barns will be filled with plenty, and your vats will overflow with new wine"* (Proverbs 3:5-10). In His oft-quoted Sermon on the Mount, Jesus lets us know that He knows we have food, clothing, and shelter needs. And then He adds, *"But seek first the kingdom of God and His righteousness, and all these things shall be added to you"* (Matthew 6:33).

In fact, for all types of work, there are Biblical principles that apply. *"There is no branch of legitimate business for which the Bible does not afford an essential preparation. Its principles of diligence, honesty, thrift, temperance, and purity are the secret of true success. These principles, as set forth in the book of Proverbs, constitute a treasury of practical wisdom… How many a man might have escaped financial failure and ruin by heeding the warnings, so often repeated and emphasized in the Scriptures"* (*Education*, pp. 135, 136). The following are examples of these excellent life management passages:

- Proverbs 1:5 – "And a man of understanding will attain wise counsel."
- Proverbs 1:7 – "The fear of the Lord is the beginning of knowledge."
- Proverbs 3:9 – "Honor the Lord with your possessions, and with the firstfruits of all your increase."
- Proverbs 4:14 – "Do not enter the path of the wicked."
- Proverbs 7:25 – "Do not let your heart turn aside to her (an immoral woman) ways."
- Proverbs 10:4 – "He who has a slack hand becomes poor."
- Proverbs 10:22 – "The blessing of the Lord makes one rich."
- Proverbs 11:1 – "Dishonest scales are an abomination to the Lord."
- Proverbs 11:15 – "One who hates being surety is secure."
- Proverbs 11:25 – "The generous soul will be made rich."
- Proverbs 11:28 – "He who trusts in his riches will fall."
- Proverbs 16:9 – "A man's heart plans his way, but the Lord directs his steps."
- Proverbs 17:18 – "A man devoid of understanding shakes hands in a pledge, and becomes surety for his friend."
- Proverbs 21:5 – "The plans of the diligent lead surely to plenty."
- Proverbs 23:4 – "Do not overwork to be rich."

The Two-Income Family

Frequently in Christian circles the topic of mothers working outside the home is a point of some discussion. Most people would agree that under ideal circumstances mothers with young children at home would prefer to be—and actually should be—at home providing a nurturing atmosphere for the growing and learning children. Studies show that children learn the most and fastest in their preschool years. In addition, most children make their spiritual commitments before the age of twelve. How important are these years of learning and bonding for the training of successful children! The Bible encourages young mothers to be involved with activities at home: *"Admonish the young women to love their husbands, to love their children, to be discreet, chaste, homemakers"* (Titus 2:4, 5).

Proverbs 31 portrays the picture of a working wife who lives a balanced life with the emphasis of her activity being for the home. The Bible does not indicate that a wife should be confined to the home but rather that her work should be activities that relate to the home. (In our family my wife has been the money manager, the homemaker, the purchaser, and the primary caregiver to our children. We all have enjoyed this arrangement very much.)

Many families with young children at home feel that they have no choice but to have both the mother and the father full time in the work force just to keep up with their expenses. Following the Second World War, working husbands outnumbered working wives five to one. Today the ratio is less than two to one. It would seem more appropriate for mothers to work outside the home as a safety net for the income stream to the family when the children are in school or on their own. Many studies have shown that for non-professional women, when all the additional expenses needed to join the workforce are considered, there is very little advantage to the family with the mother working. All the additional expenses that must come out of the income is quite significant. There is tithe, offerings, state and federal taxes, social security, transportation, food, clothing, and maybe even childcare.

For example: A full-day program in pre-kindergarten offered by the Chicago public school district costs $6,500 a year—more than the cost of a year's tuition at the University of Illinois! According to one study, the annual cost for a four-year-old to attend a childcare center in an urban area in America is more than <u>double</u> the price of college tuition in fifteen states. A mother with pre-school children must pay this high childcare cost—over $500 per month—to be able to join the workforce. An even more important consideration is the fact that the child will be much better off with mom at home than in day-care. The primary mission of most day-care programs is not to educate children but to provide surrogate childcare when the parents are at work.

When mothers joined the workforce, the family gave up something of considerable (although unrecognized) economic value: an extra skilled and dedicated adult, available to pitch in to help save the family during times of emergency. The stay-at-home mom gave her family a safety net, an all-purpose insurance policy against disaster. In fact, for middle-class families, the most important part of the safety net for generations has been the stay-at-home mother.

The stay-at-home mother had an important economic role. She made sure that the family income was carefully spent. It was her job to ensure that Dad's salary went as far as possible, and so, she mended torn garments, packed lunches, and counted the family's pennies. Her economic contribution, in effect, was that of a careful guardian of what her husband brought

home. The full-time homemaker did more than change diapers and check homework; she was available to provide extra care for anyone—child or adult—who needs it.

Two Incomes—Double Trouble

It would seem to the casual observer that with two incomes the family financial structure would be almost invincible. However, just the opposite is true. It seems that for many families, the two incomes are merged into one bigger spending pot, and they live at the very edge of their income possibilities.

A well-documented book by Elizabeth Warren, a professor at Harvard Law School, and her daughter, Amelia Warren Tyagi, who has an MBA from the Wharton School at the University of Pennsylvania, *The Two-Income Trap*, is an excellent review of the reasons behind the current wave of bankruptcy filings and home mortgage foreclosures in America. The following factoids are gleaned from their valuable work:

Even as millions of mothers have marched into the workforce, family savings have declined. Today's dual-income families have less discretionary income—less money put away for a rainy day—than the single-income family of a generation ago. And so, the two-income trap has been neatly sprung. Now mothers work two jobs—one at home and one at the office.

Today's parents are working harder than ever—far harder than their single-income counterparts of a generation ago—holding down full-time paying jobs while still covering all their obligations at home. Yet, paradoxically, without the safety net once provided by the stay-at-home mother, they are <u>more</u> vulnerable to financial disaster!

With mom in the workplace and the family's safety net forfeited, a short-term job loss or a medium-sized illness now poses a far greater menace to a family that has no reserves. It takes less to sink these families; as a result, more of them go under. But the two-income family did not lose just its safety net. By sending both adults into the labor force, these families actually increased the chances that they would need that safety net.

Two-income families are more likely to file for bankruptcy than their one-income counterparts. The family that sends both workers into the workforce in order to buffer themselves against the terrible wrenches of a changing economy has just made itself more vulnerable to those very wrenches—twice as likely, as a matter of fact.

These startling facts should be of concern to Christian families today. We all can learn from the misfortunes of others. Both adults in the family working does not guarantee that the family will get caught in the two-income trap, but it does mean that there is more risk that it could happen and that families must plan accordingly. Remember that money in the bank—a savings account—is still the first and best line of defense against any economic bump in the road.

Without the safety net of the stay-at-home mom, the two-income family must consciously be careful not to budget as tightly as the one-income household. The regular fixed expenses should be cared for by the primary income while the savings, prepayment of mortgage, family extras, and even significant contributions or charitable giving can be taken from the second income. Do not get caught in the trap. The modern American family is walking on a high wire without a net; they pray there will not be any wind. If all goes well, they will make it across safely, their children will grow up and finish college, and they will move on to retirement. But if anything—anything at all—goes wrong, then today's two-income family is in big, big trouble!

God Trusts Us

If you were going on an extended trip, say for six months or more, who would be your first choice to care for your home and other personal property needs? Would it be family? Is not our deepest trust to be found in those closest to us? So it is with God. He has called us, His children, to care for His Kingdom until He returns. *"Behold,*

what manner of love the Father has bestowed upon us, that we should be called children of God" (1 John 3:1.)!

Stewardship is a position of dignity because God trusts us and sees in us the greatest potential for carrying out His wishes. It is very much like the position of trustee of the property of another. The position of steward is the highest point to which a Christian can attain in the Kingdom of God. Along with calling us His children, God has committed to us this highest trust—stewardship. Should we not respond by a spontaneous and grateful love in service to Him and humanity? God desires the glad service of His children more than the obedience of servants. Are you serving Christ as God's child or as a servant?

Work and Time

Time is the great equalizer of all people. A day is twenty-four hours regardless of where you live. Some may get more 24-hour cycles in their life span than others, but a day is the same regardless of your economic standing, education, or geographic location. Time is the mode in which each of us operates, and it demands our most efficient use.

Many questions can confront us each day. Do we work with excellence, or do we produce sub-standard products? How do we treat our employees? Do we get our riches on the backs of the people we employ?

Time is life because character cannot be formed in a day or year, and character is essential to the highest realization of life. Time is holy to the Christian because of the high purpose to which it may be consecrated. In the case of the Sabbath, we find holy time taken to another level. Jesus healed on the Sabbath. He made it plain that His design as the Creator in sanctifying the Sabbath was for the benefit of people both as a divine gift of holy time and as a holy appointment with their Creator and Redeemer each week. *"The Sabbath was made for man, and not man for the Sabbath,"* He declared in Mark 2:27. In this declaration, Jesus set forth the guiding principle, which is valid for all time in determining the right and the wrong use of time. The Sabbath is to be used for the development and welfare of people and to <u>set the standard</u> for the other six days. The Sabbath is the crown jewel of each week.

Life that functions in accordance with the principle of the stewardship of time is the full, free Christian life rather than the routine life. Paul says in Ephesians 5:16 that we should be *"redeeming the time, because the days are evil."* The context implies that those who are wise and live wisely are "redeeming the time." In other words, a person is making the most of time when living in accordance with his best knowledge and thought.

Time makes life even more serious than death; for we are not responsible for dying (for the fact of death), but we are responsible for living (for the way we live). Time is not to be killed (as some say, "Oh! I am just killing time,") or merely wasted away or employed to no purpose or advantage. It is to be <u>redeemed</u>! Time is redeemed when it is used for the good of persons in a wise and thoughtful way. We cannot manage time because it never stops. We have no control over it; we cannot slow it down or speed it up; we can only do our best to live wisely and holy within it.

Time is a bank deposit the size of which we do not know. We only can make withdrawals— actually they are automatic withdrawals—and we cannot add to it. None of us knows when his account will be closed. The solemn lesson that the passing of time should teach each of us is not that of the self-centered, pleasure-seeker, "Enjoy every minute while you can"; nor is it that of the self-centered pessimist, "Mourn, for nothing lasts"; but rather, it is that of the positive joy of the highest work in the universe, "Cheerful Christian work!"

Work as Sacred

What shall I do with my life? Where and in what way shall I live it? *"Lord, what will you have me do"* (Acts 9:6)? asked Paul when he had seen Christ, and the focus of his life had been changed. The question of a person's life work is a question every

person must face, and the answer can impact a person's happiness and success.

In light of the principles of stewardship for all of life, it is apparent that there is no sharp dividing line between so-called secular and sacred callings. All legitimate work is sacred and has divine approval. All occupations and professions are intended to be ministries. The farmer should raise crops, the teacher should teach school, and the doctor performs his duties with the same purpose and fidelity that is expected of a pastor at home or a missionary abroad. The true steward invests his energy for the building up of the kingdom of God, even though his particular job may be as a very simple manual laborer or a highly educated professional. God is interested in every activity that makes the world better, and no Christian should invest his life in any activity that does not minister to his fellow men. He who serves well in his place, whatever it may be, serves the purpose for which Jesus came. Every honorable calling in which people are engaged is an opportunity for ministry to humanity.

Talents come in two ways—natural and acquired. Some people have natural abilities to sing, write, memorize, or paint. These are types of natural talents. Acquired abilities are those learned either through apprenticeships or other "on the job" trainings or from education received at colleges or universities. All talents should be used to serve others and to make the world better. Every talent, whether musical voice, hospitality, speaking, business ability, leadership, should be invested, not buried. God expects each one to be devoted to His service. There may not be a steeple over the place where you work, but you can be assured of Christ's presence even if you are the only Christian working there.

<u>God has a plan for every person's life and His will is discernable. One way to discover God's will is the practice of stewardship. *"In all thy ways acknowledge him,"* (that is the practice of stewardship) *"and he shall direct thy paths"* (Proverbs 3:6).</u> We have a right to expect His guidance, and He is ready to give it to us in various ways. He gave it to Moses through the burning bush, to Jacob at the foot of the ladder, to Paul

in the heavenly vision at noonday. To Abraham, Joseph, and Joshua, He gave it a step at a time. If we yield ourselves fully to Him, which is the essence of stewardship, and wait daily for His direction as to our choices and course in life, guidance is sure to come through the Scriptures, Divine Providence, conscience, better judgment, the counsel of others, and the leading of the Holy Spirit.

Sometimes our life situations keep us completely occupied. However, there is a big world out there and many need the good news of Jesus Christ. *"Millions upon millions have never so much as heard of God or of His love revealed in Christ. It is their right to receive this knowledge. They have an equal claim with us in the Saviour's mercy. And it rests with us who have received the knowledge, with our children to whom we may impart it, to answer their cry"* (*Education*, p. 263).

Summary

In our Christian lives we will:
- see honesty and integrity in all things as essential;
- know that God has made us co-workers with Him in His plan for world evangelism (the Great Commission);
- live and work for the redemption of all human life in all its forms because it is the goal of God;
- understand that character development is our first priority;
- pursue the greatest investment we can make for the glory of God and the good of humanity;

- treat all as equals knowing that no one is nearer to God than any other because of his profession, position, or station in life;
- know that it is not where we live and what we do, but <u>how</u> we live and for <u>what purpose</u>, that is important;
- attempt to remember that all legitimate work is sacred and that there is no sharp dividing line between so-called secular and sacred callings;
- believe that God has a plan for every person's life and His will is discernable, but only through prayer and Bible study and the leading of the Holy Spirit; and,
- persevere in our service to Christ.

The book, *Steps to Christ* (p. 70), suggests a daily prayer routine in these words: *"Consecrate yourself to God in the morning; make this your very first work. Let your prayer be, 'Take me, O Lord, as wholly Thine. I lay all my plans at Thy feet. Use me today in Thy service. Abide with me, and let all my work be wrought in Thee.' This is a daily matter. Each morning consecrate yourself to God for that day. Surrender all your plans to Him, to be carried out or given up as His providence shall indicate. Thus day by day you may be giving your life into the hands of God, and thus your life will be molded more and more after the life of Christ."*

Assignment for this lesson:
1. Memorize Colossians 3:23, 24.
2. Complete the worksheets for this lesson.
3. Pray that God will guide you to where He wants you to be.

Honesty, Integrity, Work

Memory Text: Colossians 3:23-24

"And whatever you do, do it heartily, as to the Lord and not to men, knowing that from the Lord you will receive the reward of the inheritance; for you serve the Lord Christ."

PRAYER TIME:

Make a list of those in your group who have asked for special prayer needs this week and pray for them each day.

_____

_____

Pray also for God's wisdom and blessing as you develop your financial plan.

STUDY TIME:

Day One

Read and reflect on the positive results of honesty and contrast with the negative results of dishonesty as shown in the table below:

Honesty Texts	Positives	Personal Comments
Proverbs 2:7		
Proverbs 3:33		
Proverbs 10:9		
Proverbs 12:19		
Proverbs 15:6		
Proverbs 20:7		
Psalms 26:1		

Dishonesty Texts	Negatives	Personal Comments
Psalms 63:11		
Proverbs 3:33		
Proverbs 13:11		
Proverbs 15:27		
Proverbs 21:6		
Revelation 21:8		

Day Two

Read and reflect on John 8:44 and Proverbs 12:22.

1. The devil is the father of lies. What relationship does that imply on those who lie? _____

_____

_____

2. How important is honesty to the child of God? _____

_____

_____

3. Contrast this description of the Devil and your understanding of Jesus. _____

_____

_____

4. What does it mean to "deal truly"? _____

_____

_____

Day Three

Read and reflect on Proverbs 4:23-27 and 1 Corinthians 6:18, 19.

1. What attributes of character are mentioned in these verses? _____

_____

_____

2. How important is character to the Christian's life? Explain. _____

_____

_____

_____

3. Comment on the above texts in light of your understanding of body, mind, and spirit. _____

_____

_____

_____

4. How is a person of integrity a positive Christian witness? _____

_____

_____

_____

Day Four

Read and reflect on Exodus 20:8-10 and Proverbs 22:29.

1. Why do you think there is a comment about work in the 4th Commandment? _____

_____

_____

2. Does it command that we must work six days each week? Explain. _____

_____

_____

_____

3. In the list of those who should not work on the Sabbath, it includes your animals. Why do you think they are included? _____

_____

_____

_____

4. Why do diligent workers stand before kings? _____

_____

_____

_____

_____

Day Five

Read and reflect on 2 Thessalonians 3:10.

1. What do you see as the purposes of work? _____
_____
_____

2. Do you think the statement about "no work, no eat," is a bit harsh? Comment. _____
_____
_____
_____

3. Since Paul wrote these words, what kind of example was he as a worker for Christ? _____
_____
_____

Day Six

Read and reflect on Proverbs 22:6.

1. Does this text imply something more than just spiritual direction? How does this suggest a parent could help a child find his/her life work? _____
_____
_____
_____

2. Is your choice of a life's work important to your Christian journey? Explain. _____
_____
_____
_____
_____

3. How would you describe an ideal job? Why? _____
_____
_____
_____
_____

Planning for Retirement

Memory Text: Proverbs 21:5

"The plans of the diligent lead surely to plenty, But those of everyone who is hasty, surely to poverty."

It has been stated by some observers that to retire at age sixty-five (or earlier) to a life of ease is the devil's alternative to heaven—if a person is quitting work to spend his accumulated assets on himself. In fact, in one of the few references to retirement in the Bible, Jesus says essentially the same thing: *"The ground of a certain rich man yielded plentifully. And he thought within himself, saying, 'What shall I do, since I have no room to store my crops?' So he said, 'I will do this: I will pull down my barns and build greater, and there I will store all my crops and my goods. And I will say to my soul, "Soul, you have many goods laid up for many years; take your ease; eat, drink, and be merry."' But God said to him, 'Fool! This night your soul will be required of you; then whose will those things be which you have provided?' So is he who lays up treasure for himself, and is not rich toward God"* (Luke 12:16-21). When we think of ourselves only and do not think of the glory of God and His kingdom, we have a spiritual problem.

However, the scope of this book—and we believe the emphasis of the Bible—is that we strive for financial freedom. Then we can devote more time to kingdom projects and helping others as we invest our surplus in projects that advance the cause of God.

Solomon, in Chapter 12 of Ecclesiastes, counsels young people to remember their Creator in their younger days—before their faculties wear out and their minds become forgetful. There will come a time in the life of everyone when, because of advancing age and its inroads into physical and mental health, that gainful "outside" employment will no longer be an option. The planning and savings completed during the working years will make the later years more stress-free and enjoyable.

From the perspective of this study, retirement really is that time in life when your most pressing financial obligations have been cared for and your income has made you financially free. Then you can work full or part-time for others and support the cause of God with time and resources.

Longer Retirement Time Predicted

Demographic studies show that today's retirees will likely have sixteen to twenty years in retirement. This covers the time from the cessation of work till the end of life. Retirement planning is therefore very important. Twenty years is too long a time to be bored, lonely, and broke. The average person in the 1900s lived to age forty-seven as compared to the average American today who will live well into their seventies or eighties. During the past thirty years, the length of life has been even more dramatically extended. This is important to know because as more people live longer, it will be harder for the federal government to continue to pay Social Security. In 1960, Social Security issued 2,000 checks for Americans aged 100. It is estimated that by the year 2010, it will be sending out 100,000 monthly payments to centenarians.

Part of the reason for this dramatic change is due to modern medical technology. Drugs and vaccines have wiped out former killer diseases, such as measles and smallpox that killed so many of our parents' generation. But it also may be due in part to the preventive lifestyle that has become part of our culture. Just think of all those radio and TV ads that encourage us to exercise, eat nutritionally, sleep better, and reduce our stress. Now there is labeling for cholesterol and trans-fats—even the dangers of coffee!

Preparation

Each stage of life requires preparation in order for the next stage to be successful. Earlier we noted that the first part of life is the preparation time—a time for getting your education and making plans for your career and family. The second stage is the working years when the children are being raised and educated and the home and other major items are acquired. This is the most intense time of life financially, believe it or not. For many families it is more stressful even than getting through college! This is a very sensitive time because the family is learning to work together and its members are creating life-long bonds. Financial stress can wreck the marriage at this point and frequently does. The last stage of life has the potential to be the most enjoyable—if proper planning has occurred. In an ideal situation the parents have raised the children to become independent adults, the home is debt free, the transportation needs are met, there are no lingering debts, and there is a sufficient income stream to provide for the senior family's needs.

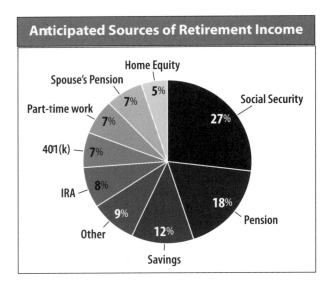

Anticipated Sources of Retirement Income

- Home Equity 5%
- Spouse's Pension 7%
- Part-time work 7%
- 401(k) 7%
- IRA 8%
- Other 9%
- Savings 12%
- Pension 18%
- Social Security 27%

Government statistics show that the average retired couple has income from the sources listed on the preceding graph. Obviously, every family is different in its income sources and amounts from each source. As in your normal family budget, when you plan for retirement, you must first list your income sources and then develop your retirement budget to live within your income. This is the one time in your life when you cannot afford to go into debt.

As can be seen on the chart, the largest income source for the average family in America is Social Security. For some families Social Security is the primary income source—50% or more of the total retirement income. Since Social Security was designed only to supplement a family's retirement income, when it is the primary source of income, the family must be debt-free and live very prudently. If you are nearing retirement age, or you see that you will not be able to work much longer, you should have as your first and highest priority the paying off of all your debts. Social Security will not be sufficient to make house payments and pay off credit cards!

The Security of Social Security

Social Security (SS) is the most widely used source of retirement income. It currently covers 97% of American workers. Studies show that 47%

of Americans over age sixty-five would be living in poverty if they did not have their SS benefits. Some people wonder about the availability of those benefits to retirees in the future. In 1945 approximately forty-five people were working and contributing to the SS trust fund for every individual drawing retirement benefits. Thirty years later, in 1995, the number of working contributors had dropped to three people working for every one drawing benefits! It is estimated that by 2050, there will be only two working for each one receiving retirement benefits. Obviously, the plan will need to be modified in some way to keep it working.

It is unlikely that SS would no longer serve the retirees who have paid into it over the years of their working careers. Changes likely would be for the full retirement age to be raised, for benefit increases to be reduced, for a higher percentage to be paid into the system by those still working, etc.

The "full retirement age" for individuals born between 1943 and 1954 is sixty-six years of age. The earliest a person can start receiving SS retirement benefits remains at age sixty-two. But, if you elect to start receiving SS benefits at age sixty-two when your full retirement age is sixty-six, then your monthly benefit will be cut by 25% permanently. If you were born in 1960 or later, your full retirement age is sixty-seven years of age.

All workers in the U. S. who are currently paying into the SS system receive an annual statement from the SS Administration that gives many details about their SS benefits, including an estimate of benefits based on their expected status upon retirement. There is a great deal of information also on the SS website at www.ssa.gov.

Retirement Needs Analysis

When you start your retirement spending plan or budget (see Estimated Retirement Income and Expenses—Monthly Budget Worksheet), you will note that there is income and there is expense. If you find that your projected expenses are greater than your projected income, then you will need to supplement your income from some other source beyond your SS and pension. Additional income sources, as shown earlier, could include part-time work, your savings, etc.

Many financial planners now are suggesting that a retired family guarantee its basic income needs by "annuitizing" the difference between its expenses and its income. For example, if your budget indicates that you will need $3,000 per month and your projected income is only $2,500 from guaranteed sources such as SS and your pension or other retirement plan, then you will need to generate an additional $500 per month from another source. You may generate cash from another source (see following paragraph), and then use a gift annuity to provide the needed income.

To generate cash for a gift annuity, you could downsize your home and use the equity beyond what the new, smaller home purchase costs. You could use the cash value of life insurance that you might have. You could use some of your savings or roll over your 401(k), 403(b), or IRA into an annuity. (There might be tax consequences here.) You could use funds from a job related "buyout" or sell some assets that you have accumulated. If you could generate $100,000 for an annuity by using one or several of these suggestions, then at rates for the average "retirement aged" couple—even with a two-life annuity—you could generate almost $500 per month, the amount needed to supplement your retirement income.

What is an Annuity?

In the commercial market, an annuity is an insurance product that is designed to provide you with an income for life. The income with an immediate fixed annuity is designed to start immediately. The insurance company guarantees that the periodic payments will be a guaranteed amount per dollar in your account. These periodic payments may last for a definite period, such as twenty years, or an indefinite period, such as your lifetime or the lifetime of you and your spouse. It is very important to remember that once you set up an immediate annuity, you no longer control the money you put in it. Likewise, while the income stream is guaranteed for your lifetime, an untimely death will not result in any money being returned to your estate.

There is also a variable annuity product, but since the purpose for an annuity in the context of retirement is to guarantee a fixed income for life, this one is not recommended. Variable annuities are securities and are regulated by the Securities and Exchange Commission. The income from variable annuities is subject to market fluctuation, investment risk, and possible loss of principal; thus, such an annuity is a poor choice to provide a guaranteed income for life.

The retired couple should have two financial goals. The first is to have a guaranteed income for life that will provide for the family's needs; the second is to have a plan to return any unneeded assets to God during life or upon the death of the survivor. Sometimes a retired couple may get this sequence reversed with possible adverse consequences. We all likely have heard of instances where a retired couple gave away funds that they may have needed later. We counsel people to first guarantee their income needs, then be as charitable with the balance of the assets God has entrusted to them as they can afford.

A charitable gift annuity is uniquely suited to fulfill the income needs and charitable intent of families. Once a family has determined what their income and expenses will be during retirement; then, if there is a shortfall on the income side, it can be supplemented by income from a charitable gift annuity.

A Charitable Gift Annuity

A gift annuity is a contract under which a charity, in return for a transfer of cash, marketable securities, or other assets, agrees to pay a fixed amount of money to one or two individuals for their lifetime.

A person who receives payments is called an "annuitant" or "beneficiary." The payments are fixed and unchanged for the term of the contract. The annuity payments are not called "income" because a portion of each payment is considered to be a partial tax-free return of the donor's gift, which is spread in equal payments over the life expectancy of the annuitant(s).

In a charitable gift annuity, the contributed property or gift is given irrevocably and becomes part of the charity's assets. Accordingly, the payments are a general obligation of the charity. The charity's entire assets back the annuity, not just the property that has been contributed. Unlike a trust, annuity payments continue for the life/ lives of the annuitant(s), not simply as long as assets remain in the Gift Annuity Fund. Payments can be made monthly, quarterly, semi-annually, or annually. Payments made from a charitable gift annuity are fixed from the outset. They will neither increase nor decrease, no matter what happens to interest rates or the stock market. The charity is contractually obligated to make the payments, even if it has to dip into its general funds to do so.

Families who use a charitable gift annuity to supplement their income have definite charitable intent. So much so that, if they could afford to do so, they would probably donate as an outright gift the entire amount paid to the organization. But they need to make some provision for income while alive.

The interest rates given by charities on gift annuities generally track the rates recommended by the American Council on Gift Annuities and have been computed to produce an average "residuum" or gift to the organization at the expiration of the agreement of approximately 50% of the amount originally donated under the agreement. Consequently, the rates are a little lower than, and are not in competition with, any rates offered by commercial insurance companies. It should be noted, however, that with a charitable gift annuity, there is a substantial tax deduction when the gift is made and the balance goes to the charity. With a commercial insurance company annuity, there is no charitable deduction. Besides, who would want the balance in the account, if any, to go to an insurance company?

In her counsel, Ellen White recommended using the concept of a charitable gift annuity. *"There are those among us who have a surplus of means, but they think they need it to sustain themselves. Let matters be arranged that these persons shall have interest on their money as long as they shall live, and let them donate the principal to the cause and work of God. Thus they will return to the Lord that which is His own"*

(*Australasian Union Conference Record*, December 1, 1900, underlining by editor).

A year later she made a similar recommendation with some additional details. *"We wish that all who are becoming old and feeble would make a wise disposition of their means, giving freely back to God that which is His own. Some need the interest on their money to support them while they live. These can lend their money at reasonable interest to our publishing or medical institutions, and make arrangements that it shall be used in missionary work after their death. Wise and faithful men should be chosen as their stewards, and clear and thorough work done to ensure the use of their means in the very way that they wish. Then they will know that their treasure is to be used to warn the world of its coming doom. We have no time to delay"* (*The Gospel Herald*, December 1, 1901).

To check out rates for gift annuities, go to the American Council on Gift Annuity's website at www.acga-web.org. To complete a gift annuity transaction, simply contact the development or planned giving officer of the charity that you wish to support.

What About Reverse Mortgages?

Growing more popular each year, the reverse mortgage (RM) is used to supplement income during the retirement period. There are pros and cons to consider with a reverse mortgage. In fact, because of the downside issues, in order to qualify with HUD, a person or family seeking a RM must first seek free financial counseling from a source which is approved by the Department of Housing and Urban Development. The counseling is a safeguard for the borrower and his/her (45% of RM borrowers are single women.) family, to make certain the borrower completely understands what a reverse mortgage is and how one is obtained.

In a reverse mortgage, a lender gives you money in exchange for a mortgage on your house. It is a special type of home loan that allows a homeowner to convert a portion of the equity in his/her home into cash. That money can come in

a lump sum, in monthly payments for as long as you live in your house, in larger monthly payments for a set period of time, as a loan commitment that you can call upon in the future, or in some combination of these.

There are five basic qualifications for a reverse mortgage. HUD requires that:

1. the borrower and spouse both be sixty-two years of age or older;
2. own their home outright or have a low enough mortgage balance that it can be paid off at the closing with proceeds from the reverse loan;
3. must live in the house as a primary residence;
4. be able to pay the taxes, insurance, and maintenance on the house; and
5. receive consumer information and counseling from an approved source.

Advantages of a Reverse Mortgage

A reverse mortgage frees up some of your home equity to spend on needs during your retirement years. It allows the homeowner to stay in his home—perhaps longer than he/she otherwise could. There is no income requirement since there are no payments to be made by the one receiving the loan proceeds. All the interest on the loan is added to the lien on the property. If the borrower elects the monthly payment option for the loan payout, then the lender must keep up the payouts even if the homeowner lives to be 120 or the value of the home decreases. But the homeowner, of course, must continue to live in the home, keep up the taxes, insurance, and maintenance, etc. The IRS does not consider the loan advances to be taxable income, and the proceeds do not affect Social Security or Medicare benefits. However, an American Bar Association "Guide to Reverse Mortgages" explains that if you receive Medicaid, SSI, or other public benefits, loan advances will be considered as "liquid assets" if the money is kept in a savings or checking account past the end of the calendar month in which it is received. Then the borrower could lose eligibility for such programs if his/her total liquid assets exceed the amount those programs allow.

No other assets will be affected by HUD's reverse mortgage loan. Only the home itself is at risk. The debt will never be passed along to the estate or heirs.

Disadvantages of a Reverse Mortgage

With a reverse mortgage, debt increases and home equity decreases. Reverse mortgages cannot be taken out anywhere near 100% of the home's value—usually no more than half if you are in your late seventies and only about a third of the home's value if you are in your late sixties. The reverse mortgage must be the only loan on your house. That means most of the equity in your home will not be available to you. For example, if you are in your late sixties and your home is worth $600,000, you would get a lump-sum payment of only $205,757 or a monthly payment of $1,110. This means that you could not access about two-thirds of your equity.

Another problem mentioned by most commentators is that the closing costs are very high—usually about 10% of the value of the loan. In the loan mentioned above, the closing costs would be $23,919! This is added to the loan amount, and the borrower is charged interest on this amount for the entire life of the loan! The interest on a reverse mortgage is not tax-deductible on a yearly basis. The borrower can deduct the interest only when the loan is paid off entirely.

The lender may require immediate repayment of the RM loan if you fail to keep up with your property taxes or homeowner's insurance. If you fail to maintain your home, declare bankruptcy, or move out, then the loan will be called.

Another negative factor about reverse mortgages is that all major programs have an adjustable interest rate on the mortgage. The rates can be adjusted on an annual, semi-annual, or even monthly basis at the discretion of the bank. Because the reverse mortgage deal is complex and includes future charges that are unpredictable, it would be hard to know, for sure, how big of a bite the loan will eventually take out of your home equity that would go to others at the end of the loan, rather than to your heirs or to God.

Finally, consumer law advocates warn that predators are always on the prowl for seniors' hard-earned money. Some predators hide behind reverse mortgage transactions. For example, it is almost always a bad idea to use a RM to buy other financial products. Especially be wary of anyone who encourages you to take out such a costly loan in order to fund an investment such as an annuity.

Other Choices for Senior Income

Many financial planners counsel seniors who need additional guaranteed income first to consider sources other than a reverse mortgage. In fact, many say that tapping the home equity should be the last line of defense. If funds are needed for home repairs or other needs and if your monthly budget can handle a monthly payment, then a home equity loan or a home equity line-of-credit are alternatives that are much less costly than a reverse mortgage.

If you still owe money on your home and are trying simply to get out from under the monthly payment, you might consider selling your home to pay off the mortgage and use the equity to purchase a smaller house, a townhouse, or a condominium. If you need some additional monthly income and your home is paid off, consider selling your home and then buy a smaller house, townhouse or condo with half of your equity. With the other half of the equity, you could enter into a charitable gift annuity agreement with your favorite ministry if you choose and have guaranteed income for the rest of your life. Even if you sell your home, you can still purchase your next place in your same hometown and continue your associations with your church, friends, and family.

The following illustration shows the average retiree household spending in America. Yours will likely be quite different. For example, if you are debt-free including your home mortgage, then your housing expenses will include only taxes, maintenance, and insurance. This could cut your housing expense at least in half, thereby saving you 15% to 20% on your monthly expenses over the average retired family! Knowing these general expenses can help you plan for retirement. Note that most Christians will have a much higher contribution percentage than the 5.7% average.

Planning for Health Care

Basically there are three prerequisites for being ready for retirement. They are: being debt free, including the home mortgage; having an income stream sufficient to provide for the necessities of life; and, having adequate health insurance.

Health coverage is important during this stage of life, since, as we get older, we will need an ever-increasing amount of health care. If you have paid into Social Security, at age sixty-five, Medicare health insurance is available at a nominal cost. Medicare does not cover all healthcare costs. Most families get supplemental or gap insurance to fill the additional need. Many workers who retire with a pension have health insurance for their families. Find out all you need to know about Medicare on the Internet at www.Medicare.gov.

A successful and contented retirement time does not simply happen. It takes a lot of planning and continual re-evaluation during your working career. Many people fool themselves by thinking that they will have fewer expenses when they retire because they will not have to pay for a mortgage payment or their children's education. But they forget that their pension does not always keep up with inflation, and Medicare does not always cover all health emergencies.

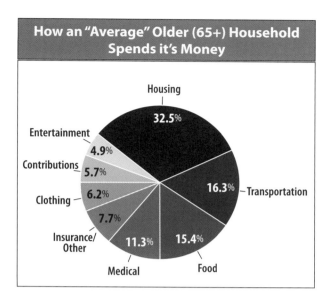

How an "Average" Older (65+) Household Spends it's Money

- Housing 32.5%
- Transportation 16.3%
- Food 15.4%
- Medical 11.3%
- Insurance/Other 7.7%
- Clothing 6.2%
- Contributions 5.7%
- Entertainment 4.9%

Tips for a Systematic Retirement Savings Plan

Develop a plan

Saving money is really hard—unless you have a plan. The best way is to sit down with a pencil and paper and list your goals and dreams. Planning for your future retirement should be a priority. Other goals might include Christian education for your children, taking a mission trip/vacation overseas, and being totally debt-free from credit card or other loans within a specified time. Once you have made your list, prioritize these financial goals, setting an achievable amount and a realistic time to accomplish each item. To boost your motivation to save, have a picture of your retirement home or a travel magazine scene of that foreign country where you would like to go on a short-term mission trip.

Don't delay--save regularly and early

Saving for retirement is not as hard as it seems. But it does demand action, and the earlier the better, as the following illustration shows. If your goal is to have $300,000 in the bank when you retire at age sixty-five, the best age to begin saving is twenty-five. If you contribute $200 per month until you are thirty, you will have saved $12,000. If you do not save another cent, assuming an annual interest rate of 8%, you will reach your retirement financial goal by age sixty-five. If you wait until you are thirty-five, you will have to make those $200 per month contributions until you are fifty, and you will have contributed $36,000. If you begin to save the same monthly amount at age forty-five, you will have to save nearly $65,000 over the next twenty-seven years to acquire the same $300,000 by age sixty-five. It does not matter whether you are forty or fifteen years from your retirement date or whether you are currently retired--having a savings plan is essential for your financial future!

Save from unexpected sources

Perhaps you receive some money that a relative left you in a trust, or you receive an unexpected gift of money from a parent. This kind of unexpected windfall could be a great boost to your savings account. Another way to create additional savings would be to have a spring garage sale and collect $300 to $500 for your throwaway items. And what about your annual tax refund? Over the last five years, the annual tax refund from the IRS for the average American family has been approximately $1,500. If you were to put that refund into savings, it would amount to more than $60,000 over an average working lifetime, or over $22,000 if you continue saving until you were age fifty. If you add the magic of compounding interest, your $60,000, or $22,000, would mushroom to well over double or triple that amount.

Save from expected sources

You probably are saying to yourself, "I don't have any expected sources of extra income, and if I did, I have many other needs that it would have to go for before putting any into a savings account." The truth is that the majority of us do have expected sources of income. Take, for example, the vehicle you are driving. If you are like most individuals, you purchased it with a small down payment, and you agreed to pay off the remainder of the cost in monthly installments. Now, what will you do with that extra $400 per month once the vehicle is paid off? Usually what happens is that the extra $400 is just absorbed into the expenses of daily living. However, if you start paying yourself by putting that $400 into savings or investment, your financial picture will be significantly different in another four years.

A man realized at age fifty that he had only fifteen years until retirement, and he had not saved one cent. So, during the next fifteen years all he did was utilize his annual cost of living raise, setting aside 50% for his financial future and 50% for daily living increases. By simply setting aside that small amount each month, he accumulated over $100,000 during the next fifteen years.

Use direct deposit

The easiest method to save money is to have a set amount deducted each pay period from your paycheck. This amount is automatically transferred to your bank or credit union savings account. The payday deduction is one of the reasons Europeans save at least seven times more and the Japanese save ten times more than we Americans. Most of us would be better off with this type of "forced" savings. Remember: What you do not see, you do not miss and, better still, you do not spend!

Latecomer tips

What about those who have waited until late in the working career and really have done very little to prepare for the retirement years? Here are some tips:

Plan to have your mortgage retired before you do. To make it in retirement with a smaller income, you should have absolutely <u>no</u> debts—credit cards, vehicle, school loans, and certainly no house payments! It will require focus and hard work to prepare for retirement if you have only had a modest income and spent most of your discretionary income on Christian education for your children and paying off debts.

For those who have not planned for retirement as they could have, there is still a basic four-legged stool that you can use during retirement. You must plan with these four financial aspects in mind: (1) 30% to 40% of your retirement will come from Social Security; (2) another 30 to 40% will come from your pension (for the younger generation it will be from those 401(k)s and 403(b)s that they will have been faithfully funding during their working life); (3) 10% to 15% will be from other investment sources such as rental property—like a granny's apartment over your garage, or one of those new Roth IRAs; and finally, (4) the remaining 10% to 15% could come from part-time work such as teaching music lessons, tutoring, or part-time employment at a fast food restaurant. It's like a four-legged stool.

Part-time Employment

In the past, most individuals and families felt quite secure with Social Security, a pension, and some personal savings. But in the future, the majority of Americans will have to add a fourth leg to their retirement stool—a job. This might not be all bad. We have a tendency to see financial planning for retirement through society's eyes rather than Biblical eyes. God's message to Adam and ultimately the whole human race was, *"In the sweat of your face you shall eat bread, till you return to the ground"* (Genesis 3:19).

In the Harvard Alumni Health Study, it was shown that among alumni who continued to work or be involved in the community in the ten years between age sixty-five and seventy-five, there was a marked increase in longevity. The research study involved two groups of 100 Harvard graduates between the ages of sixty-five and seventy-five. The first group retired at age sixty-five, while the other group continued to be employed for another ten years. The results are a warning for those whose purpose in retirement is a life of ease and pleasure. In the first group, those who retired at sixty-five, seven out of eight were dead by age seventy-five. In the second group of 100 men who continued to work, only one out of eight was deceased by age seventy-five. Apparently we rust out faster than we wear out.

There are only two texts in the Bible that explicitly talk about retirement. They are Numbers 8:25, 26 and Luke 12:16-21. In the Numbers passage, God instructed Israel through Moses that the priests who worked in the tabernacle of meeting could only do so between the ages of twenty-five and fifty. After age fifty, they could assist the other priests but were not to perform the work themselves. The Luke 12 reference is known as the parable of the "rich fool." In this story Jesus says a man is a fool who lays up treasure for himself but is not rich toward God.

In our retirement years, with all our experience and accumulated know-how, we should become a benefit to our family, our church, and our community. This is a time when we can give back to our families and our God our most precious possession—our time. This is when we can go on overseas mission trips or teach English as a second language in a foreign country for a few months. Perhaps we can move to a dark county and begin planting a church in that area. There is so much we can give of our time, talents, and our resources during the first ten to fifteen years

after retirement. Remember: *"It is better, far better, to die of hard work in some home or foreign mission field, than to rust out with inaction"* (*The Retirement Years*, p. 39).

Reduce Transportation Costs

You have noted from the earlier chart how the average retirees spend their money. Transportation is the second largest expense after housing. If you plan to have your home paid off at the time of retirement, then that will be a big help with that largest expense. But what can you do to lower transportation costs?

First, as we have noted earlier, it would be well to have a new or late model car paid off at the time of retirement. But the number and type of vehicles is also important.

What type of vehicle: Try to determine what your transportation needs will be in retirement. Then you can study Consumer Reports or Edmunds to find out which vehicles in your need area are the most trouble-free and recommended. Will you simply be traveling back and forth to town and church? Will you need a vehicle to tow a trailer? Will it be for transporting grandchildren or Pathfinders?

Maintenance: Now that you are retired (or when you do retire), probably you will have time to service your own vehicle. If you do not know how, there are many good service books for almost every make of car. With regular maintenance, you will greatly minimize the repairs needed and, of course, the car will last longer.

Reduce the number of vehicles: Most American families have at least two automobiles during the working years. However, many families find that they can get by with only one car during retirement. If you can cope with just one car, then you can save the family vehicle costs approximately $6000 a year when you calculate in depreciation, gas, insurance, repairs, etc. Being retired, not driving to work daily, generally saves some transportation costs. According to Money, November 1997, after age sixty-five, overall transportation costs will be lowered by 47%—from the average of $6,700 per year for gasoline, maintenance, and insurance to an average of $3,600.

Move to a Low Cost Area

During the working years, many families have had to live in or near metropolitan areas for work and school opportunities. In almost every case, these city environments have had costly property taxes and a high cost of living. Another way to reduce expenses is to move to a state with either no or lower taxes. Currently eight states have no general income tax: Alaska, Florida, Nevada, South Dakota, Tennessee, Texas, Washington, and Wyoming. Five other states have no sales tax: Alaska, Delaware, Montana, New Hampshire, and Oregon.

There are several good websites that give information on comparison of retirement locations. Check out www.RetirementLiving.com. One comparison reported that if a New Yorker who makes $100,000 per year were to re-locate to Jacksonville, Florida, or Tucson, Arizona, he would need only approximately 42% of his current income to maintain a comparable lifestyle.

Be Ready for Changes

The transition from working to retired can be for some a very traumatic experience. It is one of those times when "things will never be the same again." There are many transitions in life like marriage, parenting, and the empty nest when the "kids" leave home. But if you have planned for these events, you can move on and enjoy the new cycle.

One of the most difficult social aspects of retirement, particularly for those whose whole life has been wrapped up in their job, is that their personhood is no longer defined by their career. Retirement changes their sense of belonging and self-worth. As one recalled when he announced he was planning to retire, "I became an invisible person." It was as if he had already left and was no longer part of the organization in which he had spent a large portion of his life and career.

Another important aspect in this third phase of your life is to make sure you have the positive attitude that you are retiring "to" something, rather than "from" something. One of the differences for those who retire in this new century is that they will probably have to subsidize about 10% to15% of their income by continuing to be employed. However, it may be in a new field that in the past may have been just for fun—such as playing tennis. In retirement you will make it a part-time occupation teaching youngsters the skills of the game. Also, it could be an extension of your present career. If you are a news journalist for a local paper, you may decide to do something you have always wanted to do—travel and write about your experiences in a travel column or book. According to a number of national surveys, over 80% of Baby Boomers intend to continue working at least part-time after their retirement. This third era of modern life is increasingly being viewed as an ongoing process and not a one-time event. Hence, today's retirees do not consider retirement and work mutually exclusive.

Planning for retirement does not have to be an unpleasant experience. In fact, after applying the above guidelines and principles, you will discover the task to be both pleasant and rewarding.

Assignment for this lesson:
1. Memorize Proverbs 21:5.
2. Complete the worksheets for this lesson.
3. Prepare a simple retirement budget using your anticipated income and expenses.

Looking at Retirement

Memory Text: Proverbs 21:5

"The plans of the diligent lead surely to plenty, But those of everyone who is hasty, surely to poverty."

PRAYER TIME:

Make a list of those in your group who have asked for special prayer needs this week and pray for them each day.

_____

_____

Pray also for God's wisdom and blessing as you develop your financial plan.

STUDY TIME:

Day One

Read and reflect on Proverbs 6: 6-11 and 30:25.

1. What do God's creatures tell us about the importance of planning for the future? _____

_____

_____

2. Should we count on other people to plan for our future? Why, or why not? _____

_____

_____

Read and reflect on Genesis 41: 34-36.

3. What principles of retirement can you identify in this Old Testament passage? _____

_____

_____

4. This biblical passage refers to 20 % as what needs to be saved for future needs. Do you agree?

_____

_____

5. Do you think the 20 % applies to all future needs, such as paying annual taxes and making major

purchases, and not just retirement? _____

_____

_____

Day Two

Read and reflect on Luke 12:16-21.

1. How are the facts of this story similar to our modern concept of retirement? _____

_____

_____

_____

2. This man worked hard, saved, and planned for the future. Why is he called "the rich fool?" _____

_____

_____

3. What should the rich man have done with his riches? _____

_____

_____

Day Three

Read and reflect on Genesis 3:19.

1. What does this Bible text say about a person's time on this earth? _____

_____

_____

2. Does this passage mean that we should never stop working and enjoy the fruits of our labor? Should

we work till we die? Why, or why not? _____

_____

_____

Review the material in this lesson on Social Security to answer the following questions:

3. How many American workers are covered by Social Security, and how many people are working for each one who is drawing benefits? _____

_____

_____

4. What is the "full retirement age" for the Baby Boomer generation? What about those people born in 1960 or later? _____

_____

_____

5. Is the monthly income from Social Security designed to be sufficient to keep retirees above the poverty line? Explain. _____

_____

_____

Day Four

Review the material in the lesson dealing with annuities to answer these questions:

1. How does an immediate fixed annuity work? _____

_____

_____

2. What are the benefits for retirement planning of a Charitable Gift Annuity? _____

_____

_____

3. How would an annuity be better to supplement income in retirement than money in the stock market?

_____

_____

_____

Day Five

Review the material in this lesson on Reverse Mortgages to answer these questions:

1. What are the five basic requirements to qualify for a Reverse Mortgage? _____

   _____

   _____

2. List the benefits of a Reverse Mortgage. _____

   _____

   _____

3. What is the downside to obtaining a Reverse Mortgage? _____

   _____

   _____

4. What alternative sources of income could be available to retirees? _____

   _____

   _____

Day Six

Read and reflect on 1 Timothy 6:17-19 and Hebrews 13:16.

1. What key principles are depicted in these passages? _____

   _____

   _____

2. Isn't it kind of risky to give money away during retirement? Explain. _____

   _____

   _____

   _____

   _____

3. According to this lesson, what are the three prerequisites for being ready for retirement?

   _____

   _____

   _____

   _____

   _____

   _____

Retirement Budget Estimate Guide

Note: The guideline budget assumes that the retirees have their mortgage paid off and a new or late model vehicle paid off as well.

INCOME:	SAMPLE/GUIDE	YOUR BUDGET ESTIMATE
Husband's Social Security	$1,500.00	
Wife's Social Security	750.00	
Pension – 401k, 403b, IRA, annuity	1,000.00	
Part-time work	750.00	
Other income		
Total Income:	**$4,000.00**	

EXPENSES:	SAMPLE/GUIDE	YOUR BUDGET ESTIMATE
Tithe and offerings (15%)	600.00	
Housing (taxes, maintenance, etc)	300.00	
Food and household supplies	400.00	
Taxes (income and property)	900.00	
Insurance (home, auto, etc)	300.00	
Clothing/laundry	200.00	
Transportation (fuel, maintenance, reg.)	300.00	
Utilities	300.00	
Telephone (cell, internet, etc.)	100.00	
Medical (Pharmacy, eye, dental)	400.00	
Vacations/travel	100.00	
Miscellaneous	100.00	
Total Expenses:	**$4,000.00**	

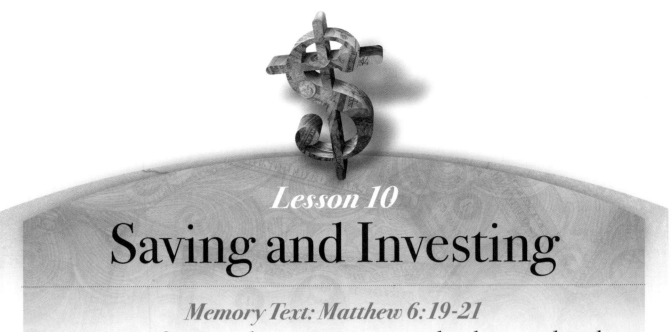

Lesson 10

Saving and Investing

Memory Text: Matthew 6:19-21

"Do not lay up for yourselves treasures on earth, where moth and rust destroy and where thieves break in and steal; but lay up for yourselves treasures in heaven, where neither moth nor rust destroys and where thieves do not break in and steal. For where your treasure is, there your heart will be also."

Most people spend whatever they earn no matter how much it is. Setting some of our income aside for future use is called delayed gratification. We plan to spend the money eventually, but we realize we must limit our current spending so that we will have money to spend in the future. In 2005, for the first time since 1933 ("The Great Depression"), our countrymen saved -0.4% of their disposable income according to the Department of Commerce's Bureau of Economic Analysis. This is a lamentable fact that our spending habits have put the national personal savings rate into minus territory! Every alert individual and family should take a close look at their personal spending/saving situation.

The decision to establish an investment plan is an important first step to accomplishing your long-term financial goals. Like other decisions, the determination to start an investment plan is one you must make yourself. No one is going to force you to save the money you will need to fund an investment plan. These things will not be done

unless you take action to do them. In fact, the specific goal you want to accomplish must be the driving force behind your decision to begin your investment plan.

The fact is, saving is absolutely essential to sound money management. If you fail to save, your budget will fail. It is that simple. Without savings you are "doomed" to the use of credit, and credit is only a delayed decision. That is to say, at some future time credit must be addressed. You pay interest every month for the "privilege" of delaying your decision.

Every budget should include savings. In fact, savings are the secret to financial growth and prosperity. If you are going to be financially healthy, you need to treat savings just as essential as food, transportation, housing, or any other item in your budget.

The reason for this is that in our world, things break, wear out, and stop working. Generally these things happen unexpectedly—as an emergency—and if there is no money (cash) to replace these essential items, then people resort to the use of credit to take care of the problem. One of the functions of savings is to provide for these "rainy-day" events. We do not plan emergencies, but we can plan <u>for</u> emergencies. Savings is a very important part of that plan.

Savings vs Hoarding

We can learn systematic savings from the ants: *"Go to the ant, you sluggard! Consider her ways and be wise, which, having no captain, overseer or ruler, provides her supplies in the summer, and gathers her food in the harvest"* (Proverbs 6:6-8). The Bible encourages savings but discourages hoarding. What is the difference? It is quite simple actually. Savings is for a specific purpose such as a down payment on a house, purchase of a new car, saving for the children's education, or investing for retirement. Hoarding, on the other hand, is saving for security. When security is the object of saving, most folks never feel that they have enough. Hoarding transfers our trust away from God to our money. We are told, *"Hoarded wealth is not merely useless, it is a curse. In this life it is a snare to the soul, drawing the affections away from the heavenly treasure. In the great day of God its witness to unused talents and neglected opportunities will condemn its possessor"* (*Christ's Object Lessons*, p. 352).

Hoarding is saving and investing taken to an extreme. The classic example of hoarding in the Bible is the story of the rich fool recorded in Luke 12. *"The ground of a certain rich man yielded plentifully. And he thought within himself, saying, 'What shall I do, since I have no room to store my crops?' So he said, 'I will do this: I will pull down my barns and build greater, and there I will store all my crops and my goods. And I will say to my soul, "Soul, you have many goods laid up for many years; take your ease; eat, drink, and be merry."' But God said to him, 'Fool! This night your soul will be required of you; then whose will those things be which you have provided?' So is he who lays up treasure for himself, and is not rich toward God"* (vss. 16-21). So, the difference between saving and hoarding is not the amount, but the attitude we have toward

our savings. Remember, *"The love of money, the desire for wealth, is the golden chain that binds them [people] to Satan"* (*Steps to Christ*, p. 44).

How To Get Started

Start with $10 per pay period, start some place, just begin reinforcing your choice to be a saver. And do not touch it! Then, as it is possible, increase the amount. To be a "saver" you have to believe that it is the key to your new commitment to faithful finances. If you are in a situation where you could have an amount deducted from your paycheck and deposited into a credit union or some other saving institution, that is a great way to start the process.

"You might today have had a capital of means to use in case of emergency and to aid the cause of God, if you had economized as you should. Every week a portion of your wages should be reserved and in no case touched unless suffering actual want, or to render back to the Giver in offerings to God. . . . The means you have earned has not been wisely and economically expended so as to leave a margin should you be sick and your family deprived of the means you bring to sustain them. Your family should have something to rely upon if you should be brought into straitened places" (*The Adventist Home*, p. 396).

A Guaranteed Investment

By global standards, most of us who live in North America (United States or Canada) would be considered rich. Yet the problem of debt is a major concern. In the USA, consumer credit card debt continues to grow. About 40% of those with credit cards are making only the minimum payment. Bankruptcies are still climbing upward, reaching almost 2 million filings in 2005. Recent statistics also show consumer bankruptcies as a percentage of total filings at 97.85%.

If you want a guaranteed return on investment, pay off your credit cards and move towards debt-free living. If you are paying 20% (many cards are increasing to 29% or more) interest on your credit cards, every time you pay them down, you are gaining 20%—guaranteed! Most people that are discussing investing are, in reality, "debtors" and should deal with that before investing. If your employer has a "matching funds" program (free money), you want to take advantage of it. Get the maximum while you are working on your debts and initiating a savings program. But do not go beyond that until you have all your consumer debt eliminated. Once your savings program is up and functioning, then you can move into the category called "savers."

How Much is Enough?

The goal is to move from being a debtor to a saver to an investor. Once you have moved toward a debt-free status and have begun to save, the question arises, "How much should I have in savings?" or "When does saving become 'hoarding'?" Most financial professionals suggest a figure of three-six months expenses in savings, although some now are suggesting six-nine months of expenses, because it is taking longer to find a new job after a layoff has occurred. We are therefore recommending a minimum of six months living expenses to be placed in your emergency fund.

We have addressed the emergency fund, but what about saving for retirement? Many people, particularly as they get older, are afraid that they will not have enough money to last them during their lifetime. They always feel that they must have just a little more in case something unforeseen happens. This fear often prevents them from participating during their lifetime in excellent giving (returning) opportunities. The danger for these people is a tendency to hoard and place faith in their bank accounts rather than in God Himself.

Within the context of this study, we would encourage folks to set a limit on their savings and investment portfolios. Determine your needs based on an estimate of your expenses during retirement. Then when you have saved enough to meet these needs, stop saving and start sharing and investing in the kingdom of God. Start by checking out the retirement budget you created

in the last chapter. Christian finance counselor and author Ron Blue stated, *"I encourage people to set a finish line. In terms of income and wealth, determine what is the most you need. Determine the maximum. Set a cap. Decide the limit of your lifestyle. It is important to do this in advance, because as our income and wealth increase we seem to find endless ways to spend or save or invest that money. This pushes the finish line further away. Determining how much is enough to live on is not so much a formula as it is a guard against excess accumulation"* (*Splitting Heirs*, p. 100).

First Things First

Basic logic would reveal that before a person can invest, he must have money <u>to</u> invest. How do we develop an income stream? This presents us with the idea of acquisition that is little considered in our "me"-focused society. Deuteronomy 8:18 says, *"But remember the LORD your God, for it is he who gives you the ability to produce wealth."* All education, all training, and the resulting work—all are designed to help us produce wealth for the purpose of serving God and assisting the work of His kingdom. So, the methods used in acquiring means will always be on the highest level with His concerns and His principles as the guiding force in our lives. It is God who gives the talent for earning, so we should not neglect this talent. All stewards should have an investment mentality that is God-focused and heaven inspired.

There are those who suggest there is something spiritual about poverty. However, the Bible does not support this idea. On the other hand, prosperity is spiritual and scriptural, but it is how it is used that is the challenge. The Bible records Jesus' reaction to the rich young ruler's rejection of His offer of eternal life. *"And when Jesus saw that he became very sorrowful, He said, 'How hard it is for those who have riches to enter the kingdom of God! For it is easier for a camel to go through the eye of a needle than for a rich man to enter the kingdom of God. And those who heard it said, 'Who then can be saved'"* (Luke 18:24-26)?

He is simply saying it is "hard," not <u>impossible</u>, for a rich man to be saved. This is a great caution to all who are wealthy to keep their perspective on God and His Kingdom. By global standards, that includes virtually all of us who live in North America. This is why the focus must be on God, His Kingdom, and the Heavenly reward.

Jesus said in the words of our memory text, *"Do not lay up for yourselves treasures on earth, where moth and rust destroy and where thieves break in and steal; but lay up for yourselves treasures in heaven, where neither moth nor rust destroys and where thieves do not break in and steal. For where your treasure is, there your heart will be also"* (Matthew 6:19-21).

Heavenly Investments

When commenting on these verses in Matthew 6, Ellen White says that people forget, *"that He said also, 'Lay up for yourselves treasures in heaven;' that in so doing they are working for their own interest. The treasure laid up in heaven is safe; no thief can approach nor moth corrupt it"* (Counsels on Stewardship, p. 209, underlined the only words in italics in the original).

How does a person store up treasure in heaven? The story of the rich young ruler is recorded in Matthew 19, Mark 10, and Luke 18. All three of the Bible writers record that if the rich young man had helped the poor, he would have stored up treasure in heaven. We are also told, *"Every opportunity to help a brother in need, or to aid the cause of God in the spread of the truth, is a pearl that you can send beforehand and deposit in the bank of heaven for safekeeping…Every such opportunity improved adds to your heavenly treasure"* (Testimonies for the Church, vol. 3, p. 249).

Sometimes we feel that if we just could invest in the great opportunities available to us, we could make a lot of money. Then we could be generous with others and God's cause. Somehow, it hardly ever turns out that way. Ellen White wrote to a man who had made poor earthly investments and stated: *"You have made large investments in uncertain enterprises. Satan blinded your eyes so that you could not see that these enterprises would yield you no returns. The enterprise of securing eternal life did not awaken your interest. Here you could have expended means, and run no risks, met no disappointments, and in the end would have received immense profits. Here you could have invested in the never-failing bank of heaven. Here you could have bestowed your treasures where no thief approacheth nor rust corrupteth. This enterprise is eternal and is as much nobler than any earthly enterprise as the heavens are higher than the earth"* (Ibid., vol. 2, p. 280).

This business of investing in the bank of heaven seems almost too good to be true. Just compare interest rates between earth and heaven. During the first decade of this new millennium, the available interest rates on bank certificates of deposit and savings accounts have been very low. For example, savings account interest rates have been around 1% or 2%, CDs around 2% to 4%. In some recent years the stock market has been almost flat, but its overall average over a long period of time has ranged between 10% and 12% with no guarantee of safety. In commenting on the current interest rates, author Ron Blue stated, *"How do these current rates of return compare to God's rate of return? In the Parable of the Sower, Jesus says that He can provide a yield ranging from 3,000 percent to 10,000 percent! He said He can produce a crop of thirty times, sixty times, or one hundred times what was sown (Matthew 13:23)."* (Splitting Heirs, p. 103).

"Those who really feel an interest in the cause of God, and are willing to venture something for its advancement, will find it a sure and safe investment. Some will have a hundredfold in this life, and in the world to come life everlasting. But all will not receive their hundredfold in this life, because they cannot bear it. If entrusted with much, they would become unwise stewards. The Lord withholds it for their good; but their treasure in heaven will be secure. How much better is such an investment as this!" (Counsels on Stewardship, p. 232).

"Christ entreats, 'Lay up for yourselves treasures in heaven.' This work of transferring your possessions to the world above, is worthy of all your best energies. It is of the highest importance, and involves your eternal interests. That which you bestow in the cause of God is not lost. All that is given for the salvation of souls and the glory of God, is invested in the most

successful enterprise in this life and in the life to come. Your talents of gold and silver, if given to the exchangers, are gaining continually in value, which will be registered to your account in the kingdom of heaven. You are to be the recipients of the eternal wealth that has increased in the hands of the exchangers. In giving to the work of God, you are laying up for yourselves treasures in heaven. All that you lay up above is secure from disaster and loss, and is increasing to an eternal, an enduring substance" (Ibid., p. 342).

You have heard it said, "You can't take it with you." But Jesus seems to be saying, "You can send it on ahead!" Paul makes it very clear in his comments to Timothy: *"Command those who are rich in this present age not to be haughty, nor to trust in uncertain riches but in the living God, who gives us richly all things to enjoy. Let them do good, that they be rich in good works, ready to give, willing to share, storing up for themselves a good foundation for the time to come, that they may lay hold on eternal life"* (1 Timothy 6:17-19).

First we must possess earthly treasure before we can, by consecrated use, convert it into heavenly treasure. The righteous acquisition of property is absolutely necessary in order to store up a rich spiritual inheritance. By the righteous accumulation of earthly treasures, we multiply our opportunities for laying up heavenly treasure. The great danger in acquisition is selfishness. The antidote for selfishness is God-centered living and giving.

We hear very few Christians talk about this "laying up of treasure." It makes you wonder why this is not a central topic. This whole idea of "laying up treasure in heaven" also begs a question regarding the Christian's assurance. Who would lay up treasure in Heaven if they did not think they were going to be there? Is it possible this is not a central theme in our lives because we lack assurance? The good news is when Jesus spoke these words, He was assuming we would be there!

Christian investing is not just about money. It is about the priority of God's Kingdom. You may be saying, "But I am not rich." Studies show that if you have enough food, decent clothes, live in a home that shields you from the weather, and

own some kind of reliable transportation, you are in the top 15% of the world's wealthy. Add some savings, a hobby (like golf or scuba diving that requires equipment), two cars (any condition), a variety of clothing, your own house, and you have reached the top 5%.

Because God owns everything and we are destined for Heaven, then it should seem that every day is full of investment decisions. For instance, when we go to the grocery store, what we buy is an investment in our health. We will be sure that our entertainment choices are those that build body and soul. We have made an investment decision regarding our child's eternal welfare when we enter him into a private church school. When we go to college to gain skills that will make us more productive, we are planning a life that will produce more income so we can provide greater opportunities for our family, plus give more to the Kingdom of God. When we return tithes and give offerings, we are investing in God's Kingdom through His church. It all is a matter of priorities and understanding our role as steward.

Invest what you must on earth.

Invest all you can in heaven.

Investment Choices

There really are only three basic choices when it comes to investments:

First, there is the storing up of our treasures in heaven where we receive our reward in eternity. We do this by helping others and making contributions to advance the cause of God. This we have discussed.

Second are earthly investments where we become an owner. These investments include stocks, mutual funds, real estate, precious metals, farmland, etc. We make money if the value goes up or the company in which we have invested is successful. (Many non-professional investors choose mutual funds in this category, since they have two desirable qualities—professional management and diversification.)

Third are earthly investments where we become a lender. These investments include savings accounts at banks or credit unions, certificates of deposit, corporate bonds, government bonds, state and local bonds, and annuities. With lending investments, we get a fixed or guaranteed return on our investment as long as the organization to which we "lend" stays healthy.

As a general rule of thumb, good investors tend to move toward lending investments and away from ownership investments as the clients get older. The theory behind this move is that even though we would likely experience a higher rate of return with ownership investments, they also are more subject to loss. As we get older, we cannot afford losses, since we are no longer in the work force to earn back what we lose.

The most important rule of investing that you should never, ever forget is that the greater the return being offered on an investment, the greater the risk of loss. This is <u>always</u> the case—whether those making the offer tell you or not, whether it is obvious or not, or whether you know it or not.

We live in a mobile society today. Many people have multiple jobs during their working years and may move several times. Pastors frequently ask about investing in real estate. Our recommendation is simple and always the same. No matter how old you are now, think about where you might wish to retire if time were to last till then. Pick out the place—maybe where you or your spouse was raised or some interesting place you have visited or go on vacation. Buy a piece of raw land or lot there. Pay it off, and hold on to it over the years. Then, when you are ready to retire, your land purchase will have increased in value over the original purchase price many times. You can either use the land to build on or sell it to purchase a home in another location. This tip has worked for many pastors.

Four Levels of Investing

Christian author and investment counselor, Austin Pryor, gives four levels of financial fitness in his book, *Sound Mind Investing*. These levels suggest a progression of investing techniques and sophistication.

The first level: Getting debt free. This is the only proper foundation for investing. Develop your spending plan. Use credit and credit cards properly. Pay off your house. Pryor states, *"Keep this truth in mind: No investment is as secure as a repaid debt. Putting your desire to invest ahead of repaying your debt obligations is usually a sign of immaturity, not financial sophistication"* (p. 36).

The second level: Saving for future needs. Develop an emergency savings fund. Develop an accumulation fund for future purchases and expenditures that you know are coming, such as taxes. Then develop a plan for your children's education. This might include paying off your house, so that you will free up your monthly mortgage payment to assist with your children's educational needs when the time comes for college.

The third level: Investing your surplus. Learn about the various types of investments. Spend time learning about mutual funds. Understand the value of tax deferment and tax consequences of financial decisions.

The fourth level: Diversifying for safety. Understand what you want to accomplish with your investment portfolio. Set goals—how much is enough? Spread out the risk. Remember that the Bible encourages diversification. *"Cast your bread upon the waters, for you will find it after many days. Give a serving to seven, and also to eight, for you do not know what evil will be on the earth"* (Ecclesiastes 11:1, 2).

Get-rich-quick Schemes

There is always the temptation when we are saving or preparing for retirement to think that we do not have enough, that if we could find some great investment, we could greatly enhance our savings and be more prepared for the days ahead. Believe it or not, there are people out there that spend all their time trying to figure out ways to take your hard-earned money from you. These scammers spend time thinking of ways to swindle you out of your money. They especially prey on older folks who have a lifetime of savings behind them.

The Bible says, *"The plans of the diligent lead surely to plenty, but those of everyone who is hasty,* surely to poverty" (Proverbs 21:5). The bottom line is very simple. When your safe investments are earning less than 5% and someone comes along and "promises" you 25%, it is very tempting to indulge. It also is very devastating when you lose a large sum with such "investors." So, like the old country music song warned, "You've got to know when to walk away and know when to run!"

But how can you tell if some innocent looking deal is really a scam designed just to relieve you of your life savings? Start out by remembering that over a long period of time—the last forty years—the stock market has returned an annual rate of 10% to 12%. When a person tries to "beat the market," generally it is very risky and should be avoided by most investors. With this in mind, here are the four characteristics of most get-rich-quick schemes:

1. There is a promise of wealth (high interest rate returns)—quickly!
2. You do not fully understand the investment.
3. You must risk money that you cannot afford to lose (like a second mortgage on your home).
4. You have to make a quick decision ("We will give you until tomorrow to make up your mind").

Many people are caught off guard by get-rich-quick schemes because typically, it is a friend that brings these "investments" to their attention. He usually is sincere and genuinely believes he is helping you out. The person selling the deal makes you feel like he is doing you a favor by offering you this incredible opportunity. So, how could you say, "No"? Just do it!

Investing and Gambling

Some have suggested that investing is the same as gambling, and Christians should not be involved in either. However, the facts would show that many Christians put their money in the bank that then invests their funds. So, are banks a gamble? Banks are insured, and they have experts that invest "your" funds. However, the returns are very small, so what is a Christian to do?

Certainly there is no place for gambling, lotteries, track betting, or other games of chance in the Christian's life. In fact, financial planners say there is only one investment that is worse than buying a lottery ticket—and that is buying two! The lottery preys on the poor and gives them a false hope of winning. It is interesting to note that generally most of the people who win the lottery are uneducated and working at minimum wage jobs. For that reason, it is almost a forgone conclusion that the "winnings" will be wasted (in most cases in less than a year). One of the great ironies of gambling is that the vast majority of those who get involved lose money. The few who do win find that the money does not make them happy and even may ruin their lives.

Gambling in all its forms is putting your money at risk in the hopes of earning a return with no rational or educated basis. Some folks have wondered if "playing the stock market" is gambling. There is a definite difference between buying stock in a good company and gambling with a lottery ticket. Gambling has been defined as taking a chance or betting on an uncertain outcome. Investing, on the other hand, is defined as committing money to earn a financial return. It also is described as expenditure for future benefits or advantages.

Investing Strategies

It is not within the scope of this study to recommend specific investments. We have included this topic simply because it is very important in planning for faithful finances. We will include some tips to guide you in the process, but just like the decision to start saving and investing in the first place is yours alone, so is the decision in what to invest. We primarily want to point out the reasons for investing and some guidance on how to get started. Because of the time value of money and the "miracle" of compounding interest, even a small amount of money saved or invested on a regular basis can grow to a large sum over a period of time.

There are many types of investing and many reasons for investing; however, the most common purpose is for retirement. As for types of investing, there are mutual funds, stocks, IRAs, 401(k)s, 403(b)s, Keoughs, stock option plans at the work place, and the list goes on. Some business owners see their business as their retirement plan and build equities in it as a future source of monthly income or as an operation that could be sold for a nice amount of cash. Business owners who do this should look for ways to build these equities. For instance, they might buy a building to house the business and thus, build up equity in the real estate as well. But whatever the plan, the key ingredient in any investment plan is diversification.

Investment Tips

Here are some basic points to remember as you continue your spiritual journey in faith and finances with regard to investing for the future:

(1) Accept Christ as both Savior and Lord.

Remember whose money you are managing. The beginning of "Christian" investing is to become God-centered. Dedicate every area of your life to His service. Realize your place as a steward and direct all your energies in that direction. Jesus said, *"Therefore do not worry, saying, 'What shall we ect?' or 'What shall we drink?' or 'What shall we wear?' For after all these things the Gentiles seek. For your heavenly Father knows that you need all these things. But seek first the kingdom of God and His righteousness, and all these things shall be added to you"* (Matthew 6:31-33). (See also Proverbs 3:5-10.)

(2) Pray for Divine wisdom and the help of the Holy Spirit.

All planning begins as close to the Cross as you can get—on your knees. We are promised wisdom in our choices and decisions. Use this Resource in your life as a steward. James 1:5 promises, *"If any of you lacks wisdom, he should ask God, who gives generously to all without finding fault, and it will be given to him."*

(3) Study Biblical principles of money management.

The Bible is full of financial and stewardship principles. In fact, there are over 2500 texts dealing with money and man's attitude toward it. That is more than what the Bible says about faith, prayer, love, peace, the Sabbath, or Second Coming. It is a very important topic to God, and He has given ample guidance for us to discover and utilize. As a starter, read again the Book of Proverbs.

(4) Work with integrity and excellence.

God has only one method for supporting the work of His kingdom. His people use their skills (both acquired and natural) to work hard with excellence and honesty. They are paid for their work. They in turn return to Him tithes and offerings, and He blesses them. This cycle then repeats itself over and over. 1 Corinthians 10:31 ties this concept together: *"Therefore, whether you eat or drink, or whatever you do, do all to the glory of God."*

(5) Develop a heavenly mentality.

"It should be our highest aim in life to get ready for heaven" (*Manuscript Releases*, vol. 5, p. 255). Remember the words "Well done" are spoken only to those who manage their money Christianly (see Matthew 25:21.) We store up on earth what we must for emergencies and retirement, but our best efforts will be to store up treasures in heaven.

(6) Be faithful with tithes and offerings.

We do not return tithes and offerings to God because we have too much money. We are faithful to God to express our acknowledgement of His Ownership and our gratitude for experienced grace. We obey Him with whom we are in covenant relation, so we can claim His promises of wisdom and blessings. We want to honor Him who is our Provider, Protector, and Sustainer. We want to be in partnership with the Almighty God.

(7) Include savings as a regular part of the spending plan.

A truly Christian budget or spending plan is one that puts God first and makes provision for routine savings for emergencies and investments for future needs. A savings account is also a hedge against illness, job loss, and unexpected needs.

(8) Get completely debt free.

The late Larry Burkett stated, *"It is my strong conviction that becoming debt-free, including the home mortgage, should be the first investment goal for any young couple (or person). Once you have achieved that goal, then, and only then, should you invest in other areas"* (Investing for the Future, p. 142). Ellen White expressed similar counsel. *"Had Brother and Sister B been economical managers, denying themselves, they could ere this have had a home of their own and besides this have had means to draw upon in case of adversity"* (The Adventist Home, p. 395).

(9) Learn what you can about money management.

Become knowledgeable about investing by reading books, attending seminars, taking adult education courses, visiting Internet sites from financial institutions, and talking with experienced financial specialists. The knowledge you gain from these sources will provide you with adequate knowledge to plan your investment strategy. Be sure to check out the companies in which you invest, so you do not inadvertently support some products that are not in harmony with your personal and spiritual standards. (Examples would be companies that are affiliated with tobacco, alcohol, pornography, etc.) There are many socially screened stocks with which a Christian can legitimately get involved. Leave the "sin stocks" to those who are serving Satan. God has told us, *"For those who honor Me I will honor"* (1 Samuel 2:30).

(10) Prepare and follow an investment plan.

Make savings a high priority. Set aside tithe and offerings, pay your bills, and then set aside your systematic savings. Finally, use what is left for personal expenses such as new clothes and entertainment. Take advantage of employer sponsored retirement programs and take advantage of any free matching funds. Have a set amount from each paycheck deducted and sent directly to your savings account. Use gifts, inheritances, and windfalls to supplement your regular savings plan.

(11) Develop a retirement plan.

Remember the four-step process: pay off your debts; establish an emergency fund; invest your surplus; and diversify for safety. Live below your income level—do not spend more than you make. Do not try to beat the market. Start early and be consistent. Be patient. Use tax deferred plans such as IRAs, 401(k)s, and/or 403(b)s. Counsel with knowledgeable advisors. Keep your spouse in the loop for counsel and information sharing. Review your plan at least annually to keep track of your progress. Exercise a spirit of generosity in the process. Refer to your short and long-range goals, and make adjustments as needed. Understand how much you need, and do not be tempted to hoard beyond your needs. Do not jeopardize your savings and investment portfolio by getting involved in risky deals and get-rich-quick schemes. Beware of those who give advice and also have some product to sell you. Always counsel with others, and pray for God's providential guidance before making any big decisions. Avoid speculation, and do not borrow to invest. Never invest money that you cannot afford to lose.

(12) Prepare your estate distribution documents.

As we learned early on in these lessons, our estate plan covers all of our lifetime financial management—from our first job till we give it all away. Paul reminds us, *"Now godliness with contentment is great gain. For we brought nothing into this world, and it is certain we can carry nothing out"* (1 Timothy 6:6, 7). So, just as we have discussed earning and conserving, we also must include returning in our financial plan. With the same care and concern that we exercise in our spending and savings plan, we should approach our distribution plan.

What the Future Holds

The Bible foretells a time when God's faithful people will not be able to buy or sell (see Revelation 13:17). What will people do with hoarded money at that time? *"The time is coming when we cannot sell at any price. The decree will soon go forth prohibiting men to buy or sell of any man save him that hath the mark of the beast"* (*Testimonies for the Church*, vol. 5, p. 152). We are further told that, *"The very means that is now so sparingly invested in the cause of God, and that is selfishly retained, will in a little while be cast with all idols to the moles and to the bats. Money will soon depreciate in value very suddenly when the reality of eternal scenes opens to the senses of man"* (*Evangelism*, p. 63).

We do not know for sure what the future holds for each of us, but we do know who holds the future and must therefore include God in all our plans. *"No scheme of business or plan of life can be sound or complete that embraces only the brief years of this present life and makes no provision for the unending future. Let the youth be taught to take eternity into their reckoning . . . All who do this are making the best possible preparation for life in this world. No man can lay up treasure in heaven without finding his life on earth thereby enriched and ennobled"* (*Education*, p. 145).

The parable of the talents in Matthew 25:14-30 shows us that we each are entrusted by God with different financial assets, gifts, and opportunities, and we will be held accountable to God for how we invested them in this life. We can prepare for the Master's return by enhancing the growth of His kingdom and wisely investing His assets.

Our long-term savings and investments are a way of using our years of plenty to prepare for the lean years in later life, as Joseph did in Egypt. The most reasonable use of our savings and investments is to protect and provide for our families, to develop working capital and contingency funds to enable us to give generously, and to become financially independent and free to serve the Lord.

Assignment for this lesson:

5. Memorize Matthew 6:19-21.
6. Complete the worksheets for this lesson.
7. Review your savings and investing plan and make revisions as needed.

ADDITIONAL RESOURCES:

Books on Investing:

Burkett, Larry. Investing for the Future. Colorado Springs, Colorado: Chariot Victor Publishing, 1992,1997.

Pryor, Austin. *Sound Mind Investing: A Step-By-Step Guide to Financial Stability & Growth*. Third Edition. Austin Pryor, 2000.

Books on Stewardship:

Alcorn, Randy. *The Treasure Principle: Discovering the Secret of Joyful Giving*. Sisters, Oregon: Multnomah Publishers, 2001

Rees, Mel. *Biblical Principles for Giving and Living*. Hagerstown, Maryland: The Ministerial Association General Conference of Seventh-day Adventists, 1995.

White, Ellen G. *Counsels on Stewardship*. Takoma Park, Washington D.C.: The Ellen G. White Publications, 1940.

Saving and Investing
Memory Text: Matthew 6:19-21

"Do not lay up for yourselves treasures on earth, where moth and rust destroy and where thieves break in and steal; but lay up for yourselves treasures in heaven, where neither moth nor rust destroys and where thieves do not break in and steal. For where your treasure is, there your heart will be also."

PRAYER TIME:

Make a list of those in your group who have asked for special prayer r eeds this week and pray for them each day.

_____

_____

Pray also for God's wisdom and blessing as you develop your financial plan.

STUDY TIME:

Day One

Read and reflect on Matthew 6:19-21.

1. Why did Jesus say we should not store up treasure on this earth? _____

_____

2. What is the advantage of storing up treasure in heaven? _____

_____

3. How do we store up treasure in heaven (See lesson)? _____

_____

4. Why is it true that where your treasure is, there your heart will be also? Explain. _____
_____

Read and reflect on Proverbs 6:6-8.

5. List the principles you see in this text that relate to saving and investing. _____
_____

6. Why would the Scriptures suggest for us to look at the ant? _____
_____
_____

7. What do you see as the lesson from the statement, "no commander, no overseer or ruler?" _____
_____
_____

Day Two:

Read and reflect on Proverbs 21:20-21.

1. Contrast the "wise and the foolish" in this text. _____
_____
_____

2. What role does the "pursuit of righteousness" have on a person's savings plan? _____
_____
_____

3. What purpose do savings play in our lives today? _____
_____
_____

Day Three:

Read and reflect on Matthew 25:14-30.

1. Do you think investing is supported by the Bible? Explain. _____
_____
_____

2. What messages do you get from this parable? _____

_____

_____

3. Some compare investing to gambling. Is this a fair comparison? Explain. _____

_____

_____

4. What words of commendation are spoken to those who invested for the benefit of the master? _____

_____

_____

Day Four:

Read and reflect on Proverbs 31:16, 18.

1. Why do you think the field was purchased? _____

_____

2. Investing is defined as the management of funds to generate a potential profit. What are some of the

pitfalls of doing this? _____

_____

3. This lady is a good businesswoman. What is implied by the statement that "her lamp doesn't go out at

night?" _____

_____

Day Five:

Read and reflect on Ecclesiastes 11:2.

1. What does this text tell you about dividing and diversifying your investments? _____

_____

_____

2. What are the benefits of diversifying? _____

_____

_____

3. What kinds of moral choices should enter into your investment plans? _____

_____

_____

Read and reflect on Deuteronomy 8:18. (Then answer the following questions from information found in Chapter 10.)

4. What is the difference between saving and hoarding. _____

_____

_____

5. How much is enough? _____

_____

_____

6. Why doesn't God bless everyone with wealth? _____

_____

_____

Day Six:

Read and Reflect on Matthew 19:16-30.

1. Why did Jesus ask the rich young man to sell what he had and give to the poor? _____

_____

_____

2. The young man asked a sincere question, and Jesus gave him a straightforward answer. Why did the young man go away sorrowfully? _____

_____

_____

3. Why is it hard for a rich man to enter heaven? _____

_____

_____

4. What did the rich young man give up? _____

_____

_____

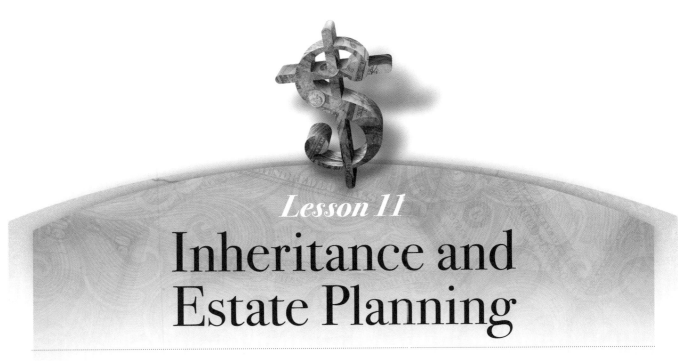

Inheritance and Estate Planning

Memory Text: Ecclesiastes 2:21

"For there is a man whose labor is with wisdom, knowledge, and skill; yet he must leave his heritage [portion] to a man who has not labored for it. This also is vanity and a great evil."

Your estate consists of everything you own. While in your working years, your objective is to earn an income stream that will provide for your family's needs, support the cause of God, and be a blessing to others. As you grow older, your point of view will be adjusted. Then the emphasis in your financial planning will shift from accumulating assets to distributing them.

Contrary to widely held notions, estate planning, which includes wills and trusts, is useful to both the rich and the poor. Trusts can be used for purposes other than tax advantages, such as choosing a guardian for children and avoiding family fights over personal belongings. Most people can afford the costs of these documents.

Many people give little or no thought to setting their personal and financial affairs in order. Most people today live longer than those of previous generations and have ample time to think about and plan for the future. Yet a large percentage of people do little or nothing to provide for those who will survive them and/or for the cause of God.

What is Estate Planning?

Estate planning is a definite plan for the administration and disposition of one's property during one's life and at one's death. Accordingly, it involves both handling your property while you are alive and dealing with the property that is still in your possession at the time of death.

Estate planning is an essential part of retirement planning and an integral part of financial planning. It has two components. The first consists of building your estate through working, purchases, savings, investments, and insurance. The second involves transferring or distributing your assets. Many people enjoy supporting God's cause through its various facets while they are alive so they can see and enjoy the use of the funds. Then the distribution at their death consists only of what is left in their estate.

There is a common misconception that an estate is only the property that one leaves at death. In reality, it is much more than that. In its broadest sense, the term estate planning encompasses the accumulation, conservation, and distribution of an estate. The overall purpose of the estate planning process is to develop a plan that will enhance and maintain the financial security of a person and his/her family. Estate planning should provide financial security during the retirement years and facilitate the intended orderly disposition of property at death. The distribution process involves transferring portions of one's property during his lifetime and disposing of property at death in a manner that minimizes taxes, probate costs, and other related expenses but is consistent with a person's lifetime goals.

The Crowning Act of Stewardship

In the very simplest terms, we can say that, since God is the Owner of everything (see Psalms 24:1), it would be logical to conclude that, from a Biblical perspective, when we are finished with what God has entrusted to us, we should return to Him, the rightful Owner, what is left in our estate once the needs of those who depend on us are met. The wise man said, *"An inheritance gained hastily at the beginning will not be blessed at the end"* (Proverbs 20:21). It is apparently better to help our children receive a proper education and a place in our business or prepared for the work-a-day-world than to leave them a large amount of money when we die. In this context, it should be noted that if we do not have a will that we have had drafted, when we die, not one cent of what is in our estate will be returned to God through a church or charity.

Most people do not realize that even if they have not created an estate plan and executed the appropriate documents to implement their plans, a plan has been created and imposed on them by the state in which they reside. Therefore, everyone, no matter how poor, has an estate plan. The state laws of intestate succession and descent and distribution are applied to the estate. The intestate succession statutes are based on spousal

relationships and degrees of consanguinity (blood relationship) to the decedent rather than on the distribution of property according to the intentions and desires of the deceased individual.

Without a properly drafted and endorsed will, a person may not leave any property to a church or charity—even if that person had faithfully returned tithe and been a generous giver during his/her life. Neither may a friend who is not a relative inherit any property from the deceased. If no relatives exist, the property reverts to the state. The property is said to "escheat to the state." Anyone who dies without a will (intestate) appears to have had little concern for property, family, friends, or any other potential beneficiary such as the cause of God or any charity. It should go without saying that every adult Christian should have a will.

Nearly 70% of Americans die without a will. And of those who do actually develop an estate plan, many spend less time on the process than they do on planning their family's vacations. The evidence is clear that, like most things in life, people get out of their estate planning process what they put into it. If we are willing to put the same energy into our estate plan that we do into building and preserving our estates, the return and satisfaction will be just as good if not better.

The Estate Planning Process

In the context of this lesson, we will focus primarily on the retirement years. To pick up a term we used in Lesson 9, this is the period of life that we called the "returning" years. Christians and non-Christians alike understand that when a person dies, he takes nothing with him. Accordingly, from a secular perspective there must be a distribution of assets upon the death of an individual or surviving spouse. The assets are either distributed in harmony with the individual's estate planning documents or, in their absence, the plan devised by the state.

The problem of letting the state's laws determine the distribution of your estate is that if you die without a will, the state assumes that you are an atheist, because only relatives are beneficiaries of an intestate estate. Nothing is returned to God through a church or charity. We are going to recommend a very simple estate planning process that essentially divides your concerns into three areas: (1) your needs for the balance of your life—Financial Independence; (2) the needs of family members—Family Legacy; and, (3) portion returned to God—Spiritual Legacy. These concerns are illustrated below. This concept is adapted from *Values Based Estate Planning*, by Scott C. Fithian.

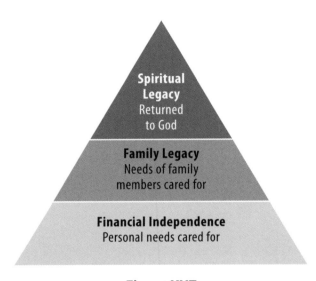

Figure XYZ

As described in the sections that follow, in order to more easily develop their distribution plan, families must first establish their needs, priorities, and goals. Looking at their current balance sheet, reviewing their family's needs, and prioritizing their charitable interests best accomplish this. Once you have taken inventory of your assets, reviewed your family's needs, and prioritized your charitable interests, you are ready to set up your estate plan. (A generic form is included with this lesson to help you get started with your estate planning.) First you will establish your objectives, then design a plan to fulfill these objectives, and finally begin to implement the plan. From this information you can develop a family mission statement. Our testamentary documents tell others how we want our assets to

be distributed. Our mission statement tells them why we have made these decisions.

When we are honest with ourselves, we must admit that most of us are not that excited about getting involved in estate planning—at least the distribution process. It forces us to face difficult issues related to our own mortality, our personal financial situation, death, taxes, and family dynamics. As a result, procrastination is not just a problem; it is the standard practice. Many people still cling to the old notion that shortly after the estate plan is completed, one will die. It is not true, of course. What is true is that when one dies, he will die prepared and not leave the family and loved ones in a lurch.

Financial Independence (personal needs cared for)

As we learned in the lesson on retirement, it is most important to determine how much your family will need during retirement so that you will know how much of your estate you will not need. Once you have established your retirement income, have a reserve for emergencies, and have your healthcare needs met, then you can go to the next steps of looking at family needs and storing up treasures in heaven.

Financial independence is the foundation of our estate plan. We cannot give everything away because we must keep some funds in reserve for our personal needs. Some families have had enough wealth that they have never lived on a budget and have never considered how much they really need. On the other hand, those of us who have had to watch our pennies will have a considerable estate when we finally divest ourselves of the assets that we needed for living. These assets include the family home, other real estate, automobiles, and personal property such as furniture, tools, antiques, and collectibles. These items finally must be distributed through our testamentary documents.

Family Legacy (needs of family members cared for)

This second area in the estate-planning pyramid has the most emotion associated with it. Particularly in America, many people grow up with the notion that when the parents die, they (the children) should share the parents' assets on an equal basis. In this section we will share what we have come to believe is God's revealed will in regard to children and inheritance. It will be new for many of you, but we believe that you will see that it is correct and, in fact, makes good sense.

Minor children

Minor children, in the minds of most parents, are those who are still dependent on them for at least part of their food, clothing, shelter, and education. There is little question to anyone that minor children should be a major focus of financial attention in estate planning. In this chapter, we are focusing primarily on retirement planning and distribution of assets that must take place in the lives of retirement-age parents. However, we must mention here that in the overall estate planning of families, efforts must be taken to ensure that minor children are cared for until they reach the point of independence from parents/guardians.

The goal of Christian parents is to train their children to become independent adults. We suggest that would include helping them obtain a college education. As we discussed in Lesson Six, children should be taught the use and value of money by using it. They also should learn the lessons of money management in family council meetings where decisions about school and jobs are discussed. For example, one might ask the children whether they would rather receive a cash

inheritance when their parents are in their 90s and the children are in their 60s or earlier when the children have finished college and are ready to start out in life on their own. If they opt for the earlier time, they can start out in life debt-free, including no student loans, and have a nest egg for graduate school or other project of their own choosing.

It should go without saying that parents of minor children should make provision by way of written documents for their personal needs, education, and guardianship. As the children mature and become independent, parents can update their estate plans to reflect the current situation.

Grown children

Leaving money or other assets to grown children is another question. It has been an area of estate planning from which many financial counselors and others shy away. Some say there is Biblical evidence on both sides. For example, Ecclesiastes 2:21 says, *"For there is a man whose labor is with wisdom, knowledge, and skill; yet he must leave his heritage [portion] to a man who has not labored for it. This also is vanity and a great evil."* But Proverbs 13:22 says, *"A good man leaves an inheritance to his children's children."* How is this apparent conflict of verses to be resolved?

It is quite simple actually. In Old Testament times, passing on ownership of the land to children and grandchildren was vital. Without it, succeeding generations could not do farming or raise livestock. Many people lived at a subsistence level. Most were too poor to buy land. With no inheritance, they could end up enslaved and unable to care for their parents and grandparents, who normally lived on the property with them until they died.

However, today in America, things are very different. Inheritance is usually a windfall coming to children who live separate from their parents, have their own careers, are financially independent, and already have enough to meet their needs. In many cases, the parents have assisted their children financially to obtain professional degrees. Most often, children are not carrying on the family business, but even if they are, they usually do not need a windfall in order to do so.

Today it might seem appropriate to pass on the family business to children who are depending on it and will continue to operate it. But notice what the Bible says about character in relation to legacy: *"A good name is to be chosen rather than great riches, loving favor rather than silver and gold"* (Proverbs 22:1). Could it be that our values are our real legacy? Parents may pass these values along to their children:

- ethical values such as honesty, justice and fairness;
- personal values such as modesty, loyalty, and faithfulness;
- emotional values such as compassion, kindness, and generosity;
- also, good citizenship, financial responsibility, frugality, good stewardship, faith in God, spiritual commitment, punctuality, competence, good health, care for others, time with family, love for education, self-improvement, and academic achievement.

What a heritage these values would be! These values help children learn responsibility and serve to bring them to financial independence. Financial planners note that it is important to remember that in most cases, grown children have the primary responsibility to create and maintain their own economic security. Fithian states, *"Leaving no money but passing values on to heirs is acceptable. They likely will manage their lives very well. . . Leaving money to heirs who have poorly developed values is asking for trouble"* (*Values-Based Estate Planning*, p. 70). Ellen White adds, *"The very best legacy which parents can leave their children is a knowledge of useful labor and the example of a life characterized by disinterested benevolence. By such a life they show the true value of money, that it is only to be appreciated for the good that it will accomplish in relieving their own wants and the necessities of others, and in advancing the cause of God"* (*Testimonies for the Church*, vol. 3, p. 399).

Christian financial counselor Ron Blue states, *"It is a parent's and grandparent's responsibility to entrust God's resources to children only if they have demonstrated the ability to handle those resources in a manner that would be pleasing to Him who is the owner of all. The fact that because you have a child should not make the child the automatic beneficiary of your estate"* (*Splitting Heirs*, p. 83).

Ellen White made a similar statement showing that each individual is responsible for the stewardship of what God has entrusted to him: *"Parents should exercise the right that God has given them. He entrusted to them the talents He would have them use to His glory. The children were not to become responsible for the talents of the father. While they have sound minds and good judgment, parents should, with prayerful consideration, and with the help of proper counselors who have experience in the truth and a knowledge of the divine will, make disposition of their property. If they have children who are afflicted or are struggling in poverty, and who will make a judicious use of means, they should be considered. But if they have unbelieving children who have abundance of this world, and who are serving the world, they commit a sin against the Master, who has made them His stewards, by placing means in their hands merely because they are their children. God's claims are not to be lightly regarded"* (*Testimonies for the Church*, vol. 3, p. 121).

Many who seek to learn the Biblical principles of money management share the idea of individual accountability to God. As we have learned in earlier lessons, God is the Owner of everything. We are His stewards. *"You are a steward of God's resources on His behalf. You are not a steward of your children's resources. You are not accountable to your children about how you transfer or spend His money. You are accountable to God"* (*Splitting Heirs*, p. 87).

Ellen White wrote two entire chapters on this important topic of distribution of our assets. It would be well to study these two chapters for details that will be of interest to you. The chapters are in *Testimonies to the Church*, Volume 3: pp. 116-130, "To (Aged and) Wealthy Parents," and Volume 4, pp. 476-485, "Wills and Legacies."

In Volume 3, Ellen White makes reference to grown and married children and their parents with regard to the distribution of family assets. She introduces the topic by stating, *"I felt urged by the Spirit of God to bear a plain testimony relative to the duty of aged and wealthy parents in the disposition of their property"* (p. 116). Then she gives this counsel: *"Parents should have great fear in entrusting children with the talents of means that God has placed in their hands, unless they have the surest evidence that their children have greater interest in, love for, and devotion to, the cause of God than they themselves possess, and that these children will be more earnest and zealous in forwarding the work of God, and more benevolent in carrying forward the various enterprises connected with it which call for means. But many place their means in the hands of their children, thus throwing upon them the responsibility of their own stewardship, because Satan prompts them to do it. In so doing they effectually place that means in the enemy's ranks. Satan works the matter to suit his own purpose and keeps from the cause of God the means which it needs, that it may be abundantly sustained"* (p. 118).

She went on to counsel, *"Parents should lay up for themselves treasures in heaven by appropriating their means themselves to the advancement of the cause of God. They should not rob themselves of heavenly treasure by leaving a surplus of means to those who have enough; for by so doing they not only deprive themselves of the precious privilege of laying up a treasure in the heavens that faileth not, but they rob the treasury of God"* (p. 120).

"Parents should not seek to have their children encounter the temptations to which they expose them in leaving them means which they themselves have made no effort to earn" (p. 121).

"Many parents make a great mistake in placing their property out of their hands into the hands of their children while they are themselves responsible for the use or abuse of the talent lent them of God. Neither parents nor children are made happier by this transfer of property.

"If parents, while they live, would assist their children to help themselves, it would be better than to leave them a large amount at death. Children who are left to rely principally upon their own exertions make better men and women, and are better fitted for practical life than those children who have depended upon their father's estate" (p. 122).

Parents who want to know how their children will treat an inheritance need only to take a close look at how they currently manage their money. It is a revealing indicator of how they will handle inherited money. Remember, your children will manage your money the way they manage their money, not the way you manage your money.

So families should take care that the amount they leave their grown children is appropriate: based on need, is specific, predetermined, and, in keeping with their value system.

The counsel from Christian leaders who have studied this topic is very consistent. It is best to help your children become independent adults, and then, exercise the stewardship that God has given you in the distribution of your property. We turn now to the third level of the estate-planning pyramid—your spiritual legacy.

Spiritual Legacy (Returned to God)

Once our financial independence and the needs of our children are met, we can experience a greater sense of freedom to consider what surplus we have for our spiritual legacy.

The late Christian businessman and philanthropist R. G. LeTourneau put it very simply, "The question is not how much of my money I give to God, but rather how much of God's money I keep for myself."

Spiritual Legacy
Returned to God

Family Legacy
Needs of family members cared for

Financial Independence
Personal needs cared for

In this third and final segment of the estate-planning pyramid, we will deal with our spiritual legacy—the portion of our estate that we return to God and store up in heaven. As we have learned earlier, we do this by helping others and making contributions to advance the cause of God. The guiding principle is found in verses like Genesis 1:1 and Psalms 24:1 that tell us God is the Owner of everything, and we are stewards of what He has entrusted to us. It is only logical that when we are finished with what God has given us, we should return it to Him. The most amazing part of this transaction is that, since God does not need the money (see Psalms 50:12), He puts what we return to Him to our account! (This will be discussed more in the next lesson.)

Estate planning is ironic in a way because most people spend two-thirds of their lives accumulating their assets, and when they finally reach retirement age with a comfortable nest egg, then financial advisors tell them they should start giving it all away. For very large estates, there can be estate and gift tax consequences. Due to the limited space in this chapter we will not discuss taxes, but each family should consult with a CPA or financial planner to make sure they can develop a distribution plan that minimizes taxes and maximizes contributions. As Scott Fithian notes, *"It is simple to eliminate the estate tax by leaving 100 percent of the estate to charity at death. Only minimal lifetime planning is required, and maximum flexibility is retained"* (*Values-Based Estate Planning*, p. 26).

Basic Spiritual Legacy Decisions

Once the portion of the estate is identified that can be returned to God, then a decision must be made as to when and how this will be done. Will it be now—inter vivos—(while living) or will it be done with testamentary documents after death? There are many advantages to present giving. Here are a few:

1. The donor actually can see the results of the gift—a new church building, a young person in college, an evangelistic campaign funded, etc.
2. The ministry or person can benefit now when the need is greatest.
3. There is no fighting among family or friends after your death.
4. It sets a good example of family values of generosity and love for others.
5. It minimizes estate tax consequence.
6. It guarantees that the gift will be made to your desired entity (no interference from courts or disgruntled relatives).
7. It demonstrates that the heart of the donor has been changed from selfishness to unselfishness.
8. It stores up treasures in heaven.

When we reviewed the personal family needs relating to Section One in the estate-planning pyramid, we noted that each family must keep a certain portion of the assets—like the home for use while living there. What is to be done with these assets? There are ways to contribute them to God's cause, if one desires, by the use of a trust or life estate. It has been said that our goal in life should be to die penniless; the trick is dismantling. If we simply wait until we die to be charitable, we miss the blessings that are listed above. In addition, Ron Blue concludes, *"My own belief is that you get no eternal reward for assets given at death. You don't have any choice. You are leaving it all anyway! How can you receive a reward for something you kept your entire life and were forced to give only at death? God will reward you later for your sacrifices now, for your faith shown now, for your unselfishness now in this life"* (*Splitting Heirs*, p. 103).

Ellen White shares the same concern: *"Those who neglect known duty by not answering to God's claims upon them in this life, and who soothe their consciences by calculating on making their bequests at death, will receive no words of commendation from the Master, nor will they receive a reward. They practiced no self-denial, but selfishly retained their means as long as they could, yielding it up only when death claimed them. That which many propose to defer until they are about to die, if they were Christians indeed they would do while they have a strong hold on life"* (*Testimonies for the Church*, vol. 4, p. 480).

In another place she states, *"I saw that many withhold from the cause while they live, quieting their consciences that they will be charitable at death; they hardly dare exercise faith and trust in God to give anything while living. But this deathbed charity is not what Christ requires of His followers; it cannot excuse the selfishness of the living. Those who hold fast their property till the last moment, surrender it to death rather than to the cause. Losses are occurring continually. Banks fail, and property is consumed in very many ways. Many purpose to do something, but they delay the matter, and Satan works to prevent the means from coming into the treasury at all. It is lost before it is returned to God, and Satan exults that it is so"* (*Testimonies for the Church*, vol. 5, p. 154).

We can give back to God now and still benefit from the gift. We have mentioned enhancing retirement income with a charitable gift annuity and continue living in your home with a life estate. In both of these instances you can give a gift to your favorite ministry and still benefit from the asset as long as you need it.

In this final phase of the estate-planning pyramid, things are different than when you sat in a church pew and practiced "wallet roulette" (checked your wallet just before the offering plate arrived at your row). The fact is that many people, up to this point in their lives, have participated in "checkbook philanthropy." They have responded with immediate gifts when the church or other organizations or ministries asked for contributions. Fewer have participated in philanthropy at this last level that requires greater thought and planning. It is not necessarily easy to give money away, but it is perhaps one of the most rewarding things anyone can do.

Christian Financial Counselors

One of the great benefits of studying these lessons, in addition to getting out of debt, planning for the future, and training your children, is gaining the knowledge of God's will in the management of money and moving into a position of financial faithfulness. Folks have complained over the years, "All the church ever talks about is money, and when you are about to die, they hover over you to ask for your last dime." A person who understands God's Ownership and our stewardship probably would not make such a statement. How we manage our money is important enough to God that He inspired the Bible writers to talk more about this topic than any other.

There are many Christians who feel that the mere mention of what a church member should do with his property is out of place for the pastor or other church workers. There even are pastors and church leaders who feel that what others do with "their money" is none of the church's business,

so they feel hesitant to broach the subject of estate planning with them. But what is the inspired counsel that we are given in this matter?

"Many manifest a needless delicacy on this point. They feel that they are stepping upon forbidden ground when they introduce the subject of property to the aged or to invalids in order to learn what disposition they design to make of it. But this duty is just as sacred as the duty to preach the word to save souls" (Testimonies for the Church, vol. 4, p. 479).

"There are aged ones among us who are nearing the close of their probation; but for the want of wide-awake men to secure to the cause of God the means in their possession, it passes into the hands of those who are serving Satan. This means was only lent them of God to be returned to Him; but in nine cases out of ten these brethren, when passing from the stage of action, appropriate God's property in a way that cannot glorify Him, for not one dollar of it will ever flow into the Lord's treasury" (Ibid., p. 478).

So who should families contact regarding their estate plans? *"While they have sound minds and good judgment, parents should, with prayerful consideration, and with the help of proper counselors who have experience in the truth and a knowledge of the divine will, make disposition of their property"* (Testimonies for the Church, vol. 3, p. 121).

There you have it. A proper counselor is one who has experience in the truth and has knowledge of the divine will: in other words, a committed Christian worker.

Options for Spiritual Legacies

There are hundreds of causes and individuals to support with charitable—spiritual legacy—funds. This is where the family's personal values, beliefs, and interests come into play. If God's holy tithe has already been returned, these funds would be classified as offerings and their use is discretionary to the giver. In Acts 1:8, Jesus gives some guidance into the scope of our mission interests: *"But you shall receive power when the Holy Spirit has come upon you; and you shall be witnesses to Me in*

Jerusalem, and in all Judea and Samaria, and to the end of the earth." You can fill in the names of the cities in your area, but it could easily match your community, your local church, your conference, and the world field.

People

As Jesus told the rich young ruler, by helping others, especially the poor, we store up treasures in heaven and become one of His disciples. Gifts and offerings to help others would include poor families, widows, orphans, worthy students, victims of natural disasters, prisoners, the homeless, the sick, etc. This is very personal work that received the blessing and commendation of Jesus. *"When the Son of Man comes in His glory, and all the holy angels with Him, then He will sit on the throne of His glory. All the nations will be gathered before Him, and He will separate them one from another, as a shepherd divides his sheep from the goats. And He will set the sheep on His right hand, but the goats on the left. Then the King will say to those on His right hand, 'Come, you blessed of My Father, inherit the kingdom prepared for you from the foundation of the world: for I was hungry and you gave Me food; I was thirsty and you gave Me drink; I was a stranger and you took Me in; I was naked and you clothed Me; I was sick and you visited Me; I was in prison and you came to Me.' Then the righteous will answer Him, saying, 'Lord, when did we see You hungry and feed You, or thirsty and give You drink? When did we see You a stranger and take You in, or naked and clothe You? Or when did we see You sick, or in prison, and come to You?' And the King will answer and say to them, 'Assuredly, I say to you, inasmuch as you did it to one of the least of these My brethren, you did it to Me'"* (Matthew 25:31-40).

Projects: God's church or its various ministries

How has your family been blessed over the years? How did you come to know the Lord? Did you receive a blessing through your educational experience or though a stay in a medical institution? Do you appreciate having a church in which to worship? Would you like to help pay off the mortgage of your church? As a young person,

were you blessed at summer camp? Have your children been blessed there? Would you like to help others learn of the soon coming of Jesus? Would you like to help build schools and churches around the world? Has your life been blessed by attending evangelistic meetings? Think about organizations working in the 10/40 Window like Adventist World Radio. Did the church help you in time of need? Would you like to help others? Have you participated in a short-term mission trip? Would you like to see others be able to do so? Would you like to support an orphanage or a clinic in an area where HIV AIDS has brought so much sorrow and pain? Prayerfully consider these questions and ask God to direct your mind to a worthy cause. You will be an answer to prayer for whichever one(s) you choose to support.

Why a Will?

Testamentary documents like wills and trusts are put in place early in the estate planning process to be a protection against untimely death or lack of testamentary capacity, and to take care of what has not been returned to God before death.

The most basic legal instrument of all estate plans is a will. A will is a legal instrument whereby a person makes disposition of his or her property to take effect after death. Once a valid will (properly drafted, properly signed by a competent person, and witnessed by uninterested parties) has been executed, the statutes of intestate succession discussed earlier are largely displaced by the provisions of the will.

While a valid will is a good beginning point for an estate plan, the will must be reviewed periodically to assure that a property owner's most recent intentions are honored at death. The birth or adoption of children, a divorce or death of a spouse, a move to another state, or a change in the assets one possesses are common reasons to revise an estate plan. Another significant reason would be becoming a Christian and having greater and more specific charitable intent.

Additional Estate Planning Documents

In addition to the basic estate planning documents, there are other life-planning documents that are recommended by most financial planners. Like insurance, you hope you never need these documents, but they should be a part of your overall estate plan. We will list them below with a brief explanation of their value. You should consult with your attorney to have them custom prepared to meet your needs and desires and are valid in the state where you live.

Advance Directives

Today, advances in medicine and medical technology save many lives that only sixty years ago might have been lost. Unfortunately, sometimes this same technology also artificially prolongs life for people who have no reasonable hope of recovery. No one likes to think about death and dying, but they are inescapable realities of life. Unfortunate stories of individuals who have been artificially kept alive for years in a persistent vegetative state underscore the reason for having advance directive documents.

The Living Will allows you to decide and document, in advance, the type of care you would like to receive if you were to become permanently unconscious or terminally ill and unable to communicate. The Health Care Power of Attorney enables you to select someone to make decisions for you. A person who does not wish to have cardiopulmonary resuscitation (CPR) performed may make this wish known through a doctor's order called a DNR (Do Not Resuscitate) directive. When preparing advance directives, it is important that you discuss your concerns with your family, your physician, and your lawyer.

"Advance directive" is a general term that refers to a person's verbal and written instructions about future medical care in the event that a person becomes unable to speak for himself or herself. Each state regulates the use of advance directives differently. Advance directives give you a voice in decisions about your medical care when you are unconscious or too ill to communicate. As long as you are able to express your own decisions, your advance directives will not be used, and you can accept or refuse any medical treatment.

Both federal and state laws govern the use of advance directives. The federal law, the Patient Self-Determination Act, requires healthcare facilities that receive Medicaid and Medicare funds to inform patients of their rights to exercise advance directives. All fifty states and the District of Columbia have laws recognizing the use of advance directives. It is very important therefore, that you have your documents prepared by an attorney who is practicing in the state where you reside.

A Living Will can be honored only if your attending physician and others know about it. It is important to let your physician and your family and friends know that you have a Living Will before you become ill. After all, a Living Will cannot be enforced if people do not know that one exists. In fact, it is a good idea for you to give your attending physician a copy of your Living Will. It is important to give copies to family and friends also, so that, if necessary, they can advise your physician that you have a Living Will. In addition, it is important that you notify a health care facility that you have a Living Will when you are admitted as a patient. Please note: you do not have to go to court to put your Living Will into effect.

Durable Power of Attorney

Another important document that is recommended as part of your estate plan is the Power of Attorney. A Power of Attorney is a legal instrument that is used to delegate legal authority to another. The person who signs or executes a Power of Attorney is called the Principal. The Power of Attorney gives legal authority to another person called an Agent or Attorney-in-Fact to make property, financial, and other legal decisions for the Principal.

A Principal can give an Agent broad legal authority or very limited authority. The Power of Attorney is frequently used to help in the event of a Principal's illness or disability or in legal transactions where the Principal cannot be present to sign necessary legal documents.

A "Durable" Power of Attorney enables the Agent to act for the Principal even after the Principal is not mentally competent or physically able to make decisions. The "Durable" Power of Attorney may be used immediately and is effective until it is revoked by the Principal or until the Principal's death.

A "Springing" Power of Attorney becomes effective at a future time; that is, it "springs up" upon the happenings of a specific event chosen by the Power of Attorney document. Often that event is the illness or disability of the Principal.

The "Springing" Power of Attorney will frequently provide that the Principal's physician will determine whether the Principal is competent to handle his or her financial affairs. A "Springing" Power of Attorney remains in effect until the Principal's death or until revoked by a court.

"Durable" and "Springing" Powers of Attorney are frequently used to plan for a Principal's future incapacity or disability and loss of competence resulting, for example, from Alzheimer's Disease or a catastrophic accident.

By appointing an Agent under a "Durable" or "Springing" Power of Attorney, the Principal is setting up a procedure for the management of his or her financial affairs in the event of incompetence or disability.

Powers of Attorney are only as good as the Agents who are appointed. Appointing a trustworthy person as an Agent is critical. Without a trustworthy Agent, a Power of Attorney becomes a dangerous legal instrument and a threat to the Principal's best interests. Make clear to your Agent that you want accurate records of all transactions completed for you and to give you periodic accountings. You can also direct your Agent to provide an accounting to a third party—a member of your family or trusted friend—in the event you are unable to review the accounting yourself.

A Power of Attorney can be abused. Dishonest Agents have used Powers of Attorney to transfer the Principal's assets to themselves and others. That is why it is so important to appoint an Agent who is completely trustworthy and to require the Agent to provide complete and periodic accountings to you or to a third party.

You are not required to hire a lawyer. However, because a Power of Attorney is such an important legal instrument, the careful consumer will consult a lawyer who can:

- provide legal and other advice about the powers that are appropriate to be delegated;
- provide counsel on the choice of an Agent;
- outline the Agent's legal and fiduciary obligations while acting under a Power of Attorney; and,
- ensure that the Power of Attorney is properly executed and meets all legal requirements.

Storing Up Treasures in Heaven

We are mortal and eternal life, for many of us, might be on the other side of the grave and the Resurrection. This "last offering" comes from having a will or trust in place. Contact the Planned Giving and Trust Services Department of your conference, or talk to the pastor of your church to see if there are projects for your local church that you could remember in your estate plan. Contact your favorite ministry or educational institution. It can assist you in getting your plan written in a way that will stand the test of law and meet your desires. Also, organize your records and plan your funeral. This may sound premature, but it will be of great help to your family if things are in order at that difficult moment.

"The Lord designs that the death of His servants shall be regarded as a loss because of the influence for good which they exerted and the many willing offerings which they bestowed to replenish the treasury of God" (Testimonies for the Church, vol. 4, p. 481).

Our Work for God Lives On

For the Christian, the Second Coming of Christ is the "Blessed Hope." We all have imagined how awesome it will be to see Jesus coming in the clouds of heaven. We are eager to hear the words "Well done." But if we should be laid to our rest before He returns, we can have the satisfaction, if we have followed His revealed will, of seeing the work go forward because of our efforts, knowing that, because of our estate plan, the work will continue after we are gone. We pray for our aged friends and family, but *"(God) knows whether or not those for whom petitions are offered would be able to endure the trial and test that would come upon them if they lived. He knows the end from the beginning. Many will be laid away to sleep before the fiery ordeal of the time of trouble shall come upon our world. This is another reason why we should say after our earnest petition; 'Nevertheless not my will, but Thine, be done.' Luke 22:42. Such a petition will never be registered in heaven as a faithless prayer"* (Counsels on Health, p. 375).

Now you can see the picture more clearly. God in His great wisdom and mercy will allow those who are older or feebler to pass away and rest from their labors during the time of trouble. This will relieve them of that terrible ordeal. It also will relieve the stress from those who would have to look after them and care for them during that time. But remember also, this older group are those who have highly appreciated assets; who, if properly counseled, could leave these assets to God through His church to help finance the finishing of the great gospel commission.

In a letter to Gilbert Collins, January 3, 1902, Ellen White wrote, *"My brother, you may not live long. Have you made your will? We know that you want to be the Lord's right hand, working in cooperation with Him. Even after your life ends,*

it is your privilege to carry forward His work. Will you please consider this, and return to the Lord His own, that you may know that you have faithfully acted your part, doing what you could? If you do this, when you are called to lay off your armor, you will illustrate the words that God instructed John to write: 'Blessed are the dead which die in the Lord from henceforth: yea, saith the Spirit, that they may rest from their labors; and their works do follow them. (Rev. 14:13)'" (Manuscript Releases, vol. 4, p. 320). According to this interpretation, the "works" that follow the righteous dead is the good that is done with the money they return to God by their will when they die. What will be said about us? Can we claim the promise of Revelation 14:13 based on our present estate plan?

Obviously, much more could be said about this subject, but perhaps this overview is sufficient for a book of a more general nature. Please be advised that it is up to you to handle God's money in your possession. Now you know there is an entirely new and different way to handle your estate planning. We pray that for your sake and for the sake of God's cause, you will become your own executor and return to God all you can while you are alive. Then, in the final accounting—the crowning act of your stewardship—you again will be faithful to your charge.

Assignment for this lesson:

1. Memorize Ecclesiastes 2:21.
2. Complete the worksheets for this lesson.
3. Pray for God's wisdom and blessing as you plan the distribution of your assets.

Inheritance and Estate Planning

Memory Text: Ecclesiastes 2:21

"For there is a man whose labor is with wisdom, knowledge, and skill; yet he must leave his heritage [portion] to a man who has not labored for it. This also is vanity and a great evil."

PRAYER TIME:

Make a list of those in your group who have asked for special prayer needs this week and pray for them each day.

_____

_____

Pray also for God's wisdom and blessing as you develop your financial plan.

STUDY TIME:

Day One

Read and reflect on this lesson.

1. What is an estate? Does every family have one? _____

   _____

2. What are the two major parts of an estate plan? _____

   _____

3. What percentage of Americans die without a will? Why do you think these people do not prepare a will?

   _____

4. What happens to your possessions if you die without a will? _____

_____

_____

5. What does the state assume about you if you do not have a will when you die?

_____

_____

Day Two

Reflect on your goals for financial independence.

1. What sources of income will you have during your retirement years? Be specific. _____

_____

2. Under present circumstances, who is/are dependent on you financially? How long will this/these

    need(s) continue? (List the names of individuals.) _____

_____

_____

3. If your estate allowed for present giving, what organizations, individuals, or projects would you like to

    support? _____

_____

Day Three

Spend time today starting to fill out the Estate Planning Form (p.154).

Day Four

Spend more time today locating your important documents and noting where they are on Form #7.

Day Five

Finish Form #7 today as a summary of items to be considered in your estate plan.

Day Six

Reflect on the distribution of your assets.

1. What are the benefits of present giving—while you are alive and well? _____

_____

2. Why is waiting until you die to be charitable a bad idea? _____

_____

3. What kinds of family values can be passed along to the next generation? _____

_____

4. What can parents do to assure that their children will become independent adults? How is this better

than leaving them a large amount at death? _____

_____

Recommended Book

This short study on this topic cannot do justice to what should be done in organizing your estate plan. We recommend a workbook that has been prepared by Crown Financial Ministries. It is called *Set Your House in Order* and can be ordered at www.crown.org. This workbook provides forms for organizing your financial matters that will greatly assist you in your estate planning.

Faith and Finance Form #7

Estate Planning Information Summary

1. List your financial documents such as tax records, insurance policies, investment documents, deeds,

mortgages, etc., and where they are located. _____

_____

_____

_____

2. Do you have a safe deposit box? Where is it located? Where is the key? What is in it? _____

_____

_____

3. Locate your birth certificate, marriage license (if married), and passport. Note location of each.

   _____

   _____

4. List the name and address of insurance agent for each policy you have: life, health, auto, liability, etc.

   _____

   _____

5. Do you have a current will? Do you know where your copy is located? List the name and address of your attorney. _____

   _____

   _____

6. List the name and address of the executor of your will. _____

   _____

   _____

7. Do you have a current listing of your possessions and their current value? Have you done a household inventory for insurance purposes? This and your balance sheet can assist you in this task. Also list your debts or liabilities for estate planning purposes. (Use a separate sheet of paper for this purpose.)

8. Do you have any ideas about what kind of funeral you want to have? If so, jot down some of your ideas regarding people involved, music, memorial gifts, etc. _____

   _____

   _____

9. Have you made any burial arrangements about which your family and/or executor should know? What are they? _____

   _____

   _____

10. Do you have any trust or other such documents of which your family should be aware? What are they?

    _____

    _____

    _____

The Rewards of Financial Faithfulness

Memory Text: Matthew 25:21

"His lord said to him, 'Well done, good and faithful servant; you were faithful over a few things, I will make you ruler over many things. Enter into the joy of your lord.'"

We have been on an exciting and challenging journey as we have worked our way through each lesson of this study. Now we turn to some final thoughts and a look at the outcomes of the life guided by the principles contained in God's Word. We want to discover the "bottom line" of true Biblical stewardship. What is success in life? How should we live? What are the goals of life? Where does faith fit in? What about motivations? Is the prize worth the effort? And, what is the result of living the financially faithful life?

The Biblical Perspective on Rewards

The Bible uses the hope of reward as a motivation for faithful living—keeping God's commandments and judgments. This short passage from Psalms 19 will introduce this concept for us:

"The law of the Lord is perfect, converting the soul;
The testimony of the Lord is sure, making wise the simple;
The statutes of the Lord are right, rejoicing the heart;
The commandment of the Lord is pure, enlightening the eyes;
The fear of the Lord is clean, enduring forever;
The judgments of the Lord are true and righteous altogether.
More to be desired are they than gold,
Yea, than much fine gold;
Sweeter also than honey and the honeycomb.
Moreover by them Your servant is warned,
And in keeping them there is great reward"
(Psalms 19:7-11, underlining by editor).

So, what are the great rewards of following God's laws? There are many according to the Bible. In this life there is peace (Isaiah 26:3; Psalms 119:165), personal happiness, less stress, improved quality of family life, more stability in marriage, and a higher level of success in one's career. We can add to that the joy of being in covenant relation with God, the satisfaction of supporting the work of God, and the Blessed Hope of the Second Coming of Jesus.

It is clear in the Bible that we are saved by grace alone when we exercise faith in the merits of Christ on our behalf. But Jesus also taught that there was a reward for the righteous. He stated, *"For the Son of Man will come in the glory of His Father with His angels, and then he will reward each according to his works"* (Matthew 16:27). And in the great apocalyptic book of Revelation—the capstone of the entire Bible—Jesus concludes His revelation to John by saying, *"And behold, I am coming quickly, and My reward is with Me, to give every one according to his work"* (Revelation 22:13).

Jesus concludes the Beatitudes, which opens His Sermon on the Mount, with these words, *"Blessed are you when they revile and persecute you, and say all kinds of evil against you falsely for My sake. Rejoice and be exceedingly glad, for great is your reward in heaven, for so they persecuted the prophets who were before you"* (Matthew 5:11, 12).

In the December 14, 1897, issue of the *Review and Herald*, Ellen White wrote an article on "Christian Liberality" in which she contrasted the rich young ruler and Moses. Then she notes that each of us must make a similar decision: *"To a youthful ruler who inquired of Him, 'Good Master, what shall I do to inherit eternal life?' Jesus answered, 'Sell all that thou hast, and distribute unto the poor, and thou shalt have treasure in heaven: and come, follow me.' This was not a hard requirement; for the ruler was not handling his own property. His goods had been entrusted to him by the Lord. The choice was left with him; he must decide for himself. Did he accept the eternal treasure? or did he decide to gratify his desire for earthly treasure, and in so doing, refuse the eternal riches?—When he heard Christ's words, 'he went away sorrowful: for he had great possessions.' He chose the earthly good, and lost the eternal weight of glory.*

"Individually, we are tried as was the young ruler. God tests us to see if, as stewards, we can safely be trusted with the eternal riches. Shall we do as the ruler did—fasten our grasp upon the treasures lent us by God, choosing that which appears most

agreeable to the natural heart, and refusing to use our possessions as God plainly states He expects us to? or shall we take up our cross, and follow our Saviour in the path of self-denial?

"Millions of people in our world are making the choice made by the young ruler. They have intelligence, but they cannot decide to be honest stewards of their Lord's goods. Many say, 'I will bless and glorify myself; I will be honored as a man above his fellows.' Jesus paid the price for their redemption; for their sake he became poor, that they might be rich; and yet, though wholly dependent on him for all their earthly possessions, they refuse to do his will by showing love to their fellow men. They are not willing to relieve the necessities of those around them with the means which the Lord has placed in their hands for this purpose. They refuse to appropriate the Lord's capital for the benefit of others, and hold fast to their possessions. Like the ruler, they refuse the heavenly treasure, and choose that which is agreeable to themselves. By such selfishness they prove themselves unworthy of the eternal riches. They show that they are unfit for a place in the kingdom of God; if they were allowed to enter there, they would, like the great apostate, claim everything as if they had created it, and would spoil heaven by their covetousness.

"Moses was called upon to choose between the world and God. Two conflicting objects were placed before him. The treasures of Egypt, the honor of a temporal crown, and all the worldly benefits involved in this choice, were presented by the prince of this world. The opposite side was presented by the Prince of Light, the world's Redeemer. He held out the recompense of reward, the unsearchable riches of Christ, and showed also the path of affliction, self-denial, and self-sacrifice, that must be traveled by all who gain this reward.

"The decision was left with Moses. As a free moral agent he was at liberty to choose. All heaven was interested in the matter. What would be his choice?--obedience to God, with the eternal recompense of reward, or obedience to that most agreeable to his own will? 'By faith Moses, when he was come to years, refused to be called the son of Pharaoh's daughter; choosing rather to suffer affliction with the people of God, than to enjoy the pleasures of sin for a season; esteeming the reproach of Christ greater riches than

the treasures in Egypt: for he had respect unto the recompense of the reward.'"

Talk about delayed gratification, wisdom, and foresight! Moses made the decision to be a part of God's people, knowing he would face suffering and hardship rather than be a ruler in Egypt and enjoy a life of wealth and ease. Why would anyone ever make such a choice? The reason he gave was that *"he had respect unto the recompense of the reward"* (see Hebrews 11:24-26). The bottom line is that the rich young ruler clung to his earthly possessions and lost his eternal reward. Moses, on the other hand, laid aside earthly riches for his reward in heaven. His wisdom is reflected in the decision of the man who found the treasure hidden in a field: *"For joy over it he goes and sells all that he has and buys that field"* (Matthew 13:44). What he gave up was nothing compared to what he gained! He was happy to make the trade.

Paul's Eye on the Prize

Paul also saw beyond the shipwrecks, the beatings, and the imprisonments. His hope of a reward in heaven is very evident throughout his writings. As an encouragement to others he wrote, *"Therefore, my beloved brethren, be steadfast, immovable, always abounding in the work of the Lord, knowing that your labor is not in vain in the Lord"* (1 Corinthians 15:58). Earlier in this same letter he told the believers in Corinth, *"Each one will receive his own reward according to his own labor"* (1 Corinthians 3:8).

In Hebrews 11, the famous "faith chapter," Paul states, *"Without faith it is impossible to please Him, for he who comes to God must believe that He is, and that He is a rewarder of those who diligently seek Him"* (Hebrews 11:6). And then after discussing the faith of Abel, Enoch, Noah, and Abraham and Sarah, Paul notes, *"These all died in the faith, not having received the promises, but having seen them afar off were assured of them, embraced them, and confessed that they were strangers and pilgrims on the earth"* (Hebrews 11:13).

Paul was excited about what God has planned for the faithful. He apparently took comfort in his afflictions from the promises in the book of Isaiah regarding heaven and the new earth. He wrote,

"But as it is written: Eye has not seen, nor ear heard, nor have entered into the heart of man the things which God has prepared for those who love Him" (1 Corinthians 2:9). And so his commitment was, *"I press toward the goal for the prize of the upward call of God in Christ Jesus"* (Philippians 3:14).

In his last letter, written from prison just before he lost his life, Paul still speaks of his commitment and his confidence in God to fulfill His promises at the Second Coming: *"For this reason I also suffer these things; nevertheless I am not ashamed, for I know whom I have believed and am persuaded that He is able to keep what I have committed to Him until that day. . . . I have fought the good fight, I have finished the race, I have kept the faith. Finally, there is laid up for me the crown of righteousness, which the Lord, the righteous Judge, will give to me on that Day, and not to me only but also to all who have loved His appearing"* (2 Timothy 1:12; 4:7, 8).

Our Account in Heaven

It should be clear to all that we each have an account in heaven. There is a ledger there where God keeps a record. The parable of the talents gives an insight to this fact: *"For the kingdom of heaven is like a man traveling to a far country, who called his own servants and delivered his goods to them. . . . After a long time, the lord of those servants came and settled accounts with them"* (Matthew 25:14,19).

Two interesting statements from Ellen White add to this matter: *"Many of the people of God are stupefied by the spirit of the world, and are denying their faith by their works. They cultivate a love for money, for houses and lands, until it absorbs the powers of mind and being, and shuts out love for the Creator and for souls for whom Christ died. The god of this world has blinded their eyes; their eternal interests are made secondary; and brain, bone, and muscle are taxed to the utmost to increase their worldly possessions. And all this accumulation of cares and burdens is borne in direct violation of the injunction of Christ, who said, 'Lay not up for yourselves treasures upon earth, where moth and rust doth corrupt, and where thieves break through and steal.'*

*"They forget that He said also, 'Lay up **for yourselves** (italics in original) treasures in heaven;' that in so doing they are working for their own interest. The treasure laid up in heaven is safe; no thief can approach nor moth corrupt it. But their treasure is upon the earth, and their affections are upon their treasure"* (Counsels on Stewardship, p. 209, underlining by editor).

"Christ entreats, 'Lay up for yourselves treasures in heaven.' This work of transferring your possessions to the world above, is worthy of all your best energies. It is of the highest importance, and involves your eternal interests. That which you bestow in the cause of God is not lost. All that is given for the salvation of souls and the glory of God, is invested in the most successful enterprise in this life and in the life to come. Your talents of gold and silver, if given to the exchangers, are gaining continually in value, which will be registered to your account in the kingdom of heaven. You are to be the recipients of the eternal wealth that has increased in the hands of the exchangers. In giving to the work of God, you are laying up for yourselves treasures in heaven. All that you lay up above is secure from disaster and loss, and is increasing to an eternal, an enduring substance" (Ibid., p. 342, underlining by editor).

What does it mean that what we lay up in heaven is "increasing"? An answer is given in *Testimonies to the Church*, vol. 2, p. 660: *"In order to advance the cause of God, means are necessary. God has provided for this necessity by placing an abundance in the hands of His agents to use in any department of the work where it may be required in the labor of saving souls. Every soul saved is a talent gained. If truly converted, the one brought to a knowledge of the truth will, in his turn, use the talents of influence and of means which God has given him, in working for the salvation of his fellow men. He will engage with earnestness in the great work of enlightening those who are in darkness and error. He will be instrumental in saving souls. Thus the talents of influence and means are continually exchanging and constantly increasing. When the Master comes, the faithful servant is prepared to return Him both principal and interest. By his fruits he can show the increase of talents that he has gained to return to the Master. The faithful servant will then have done*

his work, and the Master, whose reward is with Him to give every man according as his work shall be, will return to that faithful servant both principal and interest" (underlining by editor).

This is a very interesting business arrangement. What we store up in heaven by helping others and making contributions to advance the cause of God, and though it all belongs to God, He treats it as a loan and gives it back as part of our reward in heaven—both principal and interest! What an awesome arrangement! What a powerful motivation to store up treasures in heaven!

Speaking of motivation—note this relevant statement: *"We are stewards of God's possessions; they are not ours to use for the gratification of corrupt desires, for selfish indulgences. All Heaven is watching with interest to see what use we are making of God's entrusted talents. If we lay up treasure in heaven, we shall use the Lord's goods to advance his cause, to save souls, and to bless humanity, and all that is so used the Lord will place to our account in the bank that never fails. When the heart loves God supremely, property is no hindrance to advancement in the Christian warfare, because the consecrated man will discern the best investments to make, and will use his wealth to bless the children of God."* (Now comes the very interesting part on motivation.) *"Oh, let us contemplate the amazing sacrifice that has been made for us! Let us try to appreciate the labor and energy Heaven is expending to reclaim the lost, and bring them back to the Father's house. Motives stronger, and agencies more powerful, could never be brought into operation,--the enjoyment of heaven, the exceeding rewards for right-doing, the society of angels, the communion and love of God and his Son, the elevation and extension of all our powers throughout eternal ages; and it hath not 'entered into the heart of man, the things which God hath prepared for them that love him.' Are these not mighty incentives and encouragements to urge us to give our heart's loving service to our Creator and Redeemer?*

"And on the other hand the judgments of God pronounced against sin, the inevitable retribution, the degradation of our characters, and the final destruction, are presented in his word to warn us against the service of Satan" (Bible Echo and Signs of the Times, February 15, 1889, underlining by editor).

So, how is your heavenly account right now? Is it growing or in arrears? We should know the state of our affairs in heaven: *"Do not, my brother, neglect a plain duty revealed to you in the oracles of God. The books of heaven will reveal the fact in the past and the present standing of your accounts with God. Be strictly honest with your Maker in tithes and in offerings. You have been moved by the Spirit of God, and under the influence of His Spirit you have made pledges. Then while you have means in your hands, make your account straight with God. Now God looks at all these transactions that bear any relation to the work and the cause of God"* (*Manuscript Releases*, vol. 20, p. 371, underlining by editor).

The Growth of Treasures in Heaven

The Bible records the story of the rich young ruler in all three of the synoptic gospels (Matthew 19, Mark 10, and Luke 18). In each recounting of this story, Jesus is quoted as telling the rich young man that if he would sell his earthly possessions and help the poor, he would have treasure in heaven. As we have quoted many times in this book, Matthew 6:20 encourages us to store up for ourselves treasures in heaven.

We have found some very interesting statements about our treasure and rewards in heaven. We seldom talk about this because it may seem selfish. But in fact we are told, *"A fear of making the future inheritance seem too material has led many to spiritualize away the very truths which lead us to look upon it as our home. Christ assured His disciples that He went to prepare mansions for them in the Father's house. Those who accept the teachings of God's word will not be wholly ignorant concerning the heavenly abode.... Human language is inadequate to describe the reward of the righteous. It will be known only to those who behold it. No finite mind can comprehend the glory of the Paradise of God.*

"In the Bible the inheritance of the saved is called a country. There the heavenly Shepherd leads His flock to fountains of living waters. The tree of life yields its fruit every month, and the leaves of the tree are for the service of the nations. There are ever-flowing streams, clear as crystal, and beside them waving trees cast their shadows upon the paths prepared for the ransomed of the Lord. There the widespreading plains swell into hills of beauty, and the mountains of God rear their lofty summits. On those peaceful plains, beside those living streams, God's people, so long pilgrims and wanderers, shall find a home.

"There are homes for the pilgrims of earth. There are robes for the righteous, with crowns of glory and palms of victory. All that has perplexed us in the providences of God will in the world to come be made plain. The things hard to be understood will then find explanation. The mysteries of grace will unfold before us. Where our finite minds discovered only confusion and broken promises, we shall see the most perfect and beautiful harmony. We shall know that infinite love ordered the experiences that seemed most trying. As we realize the tender care of Him who makes all things work together for our good, we shall rejoice with joy unspeakable and full of glory....

"We are homeward bound. He who loved us so much as to die for us hath builded for us a city. The New Jerusalem is our place of rest. There will be no sadness in the City of God. No wail of sorrow, no dirge of crushed hopes and buried affections, will evermore be heard. Soon the garments of heaviness will be changed for the wedding garment. Soon we shall witness the coronation of our King. Those whose lives have been hidden with Christ, those who on this earth have fought the good fight of faith, will shine forth with the Redeemer's glory in the kingdom of God" (*The Adventist Home*, pp. 541-543, underlining by editor).

What About Safety

When we invest on the earth, we must always be concerned about risk as Matthew 6:19 explains. We even talk about "relative risk" where interest rates are concerned. We know that the promise of a high interest rate is always accompanied with high risk, just as investments that are touted to "beat the market" also are at greater risk of loss. But, what about the investments that are stored up in heaven? We have found some amazing answers:

"Those who really feel an interest in the cause of God, and are willing to venture something for its advancement, will find it a sure and safe investment. Some will have a hundredfold in this life, and in the world to come life everlasting. But all will not receive their hundredfold in this life, because they cannot bear it. If entrusted with much, they would become unwise stewards. The Lord withholds it for their good; *but their treasure in heaven will be secure.* How much better is such an investment as this" (*Counsels on Stewardship*, p.232, underlining by editor)!

We all can imagine scenarios in the economy, acts of terrorism, or natural disasters in which our temporal security could be lost in an instant. In fact, we see it daily in the news around the world. *"Everything that is laid up upon earth may be swept away in a moment; but nothing can disturb the treasure that is laid up in heaven"* (*Our High Calling*, p. 195). People who cling to their earthly treasure will eventually lose everything. But those who are smart will transfer their assets to their new home in heaven.

There always is the temptation to think, "If I can just make it big on this investment, then I will be generous with the cause of God." Unfortunately, the big return always seems just one investment deal away. To a man who had lost a great deal of money in earthly investments, Ellen White wrote, *"You have made large investments in uncertain enterprises. Satan blinded your eyes so that you could not see that these enterprises would yield you no returns. The enterprise of securing eternal life did not awaken your interest. Here you could have expended means, and run no risks, met no disappointments, and in the end would have received immense profits.* Here you could have invested in the never-failing bank of heaven. Here you could have bestowed your treasures where no thief approacheth nor rust corrupteth. This enterprise is eternal and is as much nobler than any earthly enterprise as the heavens are higher than the earth" (*Testimonies for the Church*, vol. 2, p. 280, underlining by the editor).

She made a follow-up statement regarding the bank of heaven with these words: *"Put your money in the bank of heaven. Thus invested, it will yield an infinitely higher rate of interest than if placed in the banks of this world"* (*Review and Herald*, May 27, 1902, underlining by editor).

What a Reward!

A quick check in the Spirit of Prophecy with "rewards" as the search word finds, "my reward", "immortal reward", "rich reward", "glorious reward", "great reward", "heavenly reward", "overcomer's reward", and "final reward". Check it out for yourself and enjoy the search.

Sometimes we may wonder whether God notes what we do here and whether or not it is appropriate to support what may seem to be a lukewarm church. Note this important answer: *"I was shown that the recording angel makes a faithful record of every offering dedicated to God, and put into the treasury, and also of the final result of the means thus bestowed.* The eye of God takes cognizance of every farthing devoted to His cause, and of the willingness or reluctance of the giver. The motive in giving is also chronicled. Those self-sacrificing, consecrated ones who render back to God the things that are His, as He requires of them, *will be rewarded according to their works.* Even though the means thus consecrated be misapplied, so that it does not accomplish the object which the donor had in view— the glory of God and the salvation of souls—those who made the sacrifice in sincerity of soul, with an eye single to the glory of God, will not lose their reward.

"Every opportunity to help a brother in need, or to aid the cause of God in the spread of the truth, is a pearl that you can send beforehand, and deposit in the bank of heaven for safe keeping. God is testing and proving you. He has been giving His blessings to you with a lavish hand, and is now watching to see what use you are making of them, to see if you will help those who need help, and if you will feel the worth of souls, and do what you can with the means that He has entrusted to you. Every such opportunity improved adds to your heavenly treasure" (*Christian Service*, p. 221, underlining by editor).

The reward from God to His faithful people is very unique and, like many spiritual things, may be beyond our finite understanding. We know that the gift of God is eternal life but apparently there is even more. Consider this sentence: *"The Lord has a great work to be done, and He will bequeath the most in the future life to those who do the most faithful, willing service in the present life"* (*Christ's Object*

Lessons, p. 330, underlining by editor). You cannot get more of eternal life than eternal life!

But do not get the reward confused with merit. The only merit we ever have is that of Jesus' extended on our behalf. In one of her morning devotionals to the ministers assembled for the General Conference Session held in Battle Creek in November of 1883, Ellen White stated, *"We shall none of us be saved for our own merits; the rewards of eternity are purchased by Christ, and in no case merited by man; yet ministers should remember that every man will receive according as his works have been. The trials of the great assize will proceed most accurately on the basis of works, and our listlessness and want of zeal will tell on its decisions. The parable of the talents illustrates this subject. One man becomes ruler over ten cities, another over five, another over two. Each receives in exact proportion to his work—to the improvement he has made on the talents lent him of God; and it is the privilege of each to strive for the highest recompense"* (*Gospel Workers*, p. 450, underlining by editor).

To put our reward in its proper place, we must remember that it should not be our primary motive for obedience. Our obedience is a "service and allegiance of love" (Steps to Christ, p. 60). But when commenting on the story Jesus told of the workers who worked different hours of the day and each received a "penny", Ellen White noted, *"In a subordinate sense we should all have respect unto the recompense of the reward. But while we appreciate the promise of blessing, we should have perfect confidence in Jesus Christ, believing that He will do right, and give us reward according as our works have been. The gift of God is eternal life, but Jesus would have us not so anxious concerning rewards, as that we may do the will of God because it is right to do it, irrespective of all gain"* (*Counsels on Stewardship*, p. 339).

Bible prophecy informs us that the last generation on earth before the second coming of Christ will go through a time of trouble that is worse than anything ever experienced before (see Daniel 12:1). What will keep people buoyed up through this period? It is the knowledge that God has plans for us that are beyond our ability to comprehend.

A Good Steward of the Gospel

David Livingstone, the great Scottish missionary to Africa, said, *"I will place no value on anything I have or may possess, except in its relation to the kingdom of Christ. If anything I have will advance the interests of that kingdom, it shall be given up or kept, as by keeping or giving it I shall most promote the glory of him to whom I owe all my hopes, both of time and eternity."* This would be a terrific life purpose statement for all desiring to be faithful stewards.

Ellen White expressed a similar sentiment, *"Consecrate yourself to God in the morning; make this your very first work. Let your prayer be, 'Take me, O Lord, as wholly Thine. I lay all my plans at Thy feet. Use me today in Thy service. Abide with me, and let all my work be wrought in Thee.' This is a daily matter. Each morning consecrate yourself to God for that day. Surrender all your plans to Him, to be carried out or given up as His providence shall indicate. Thus day by day you may be giving your life into the hands of God, and thus your life will be molded more and more after the life of Christ"* (*Steps to Christ*, p. 70).

Another statement that is worthy of our consideration says, *"A steward identifies himself with his master. He accepts the responsibilities of a steward, and he must act in his master's stead, doing as his master would do were he presiding. His master's interests become his. The position of a steward is one of dignity, because his master trusts him. If in any wise he acts selfishly, and turns the advantages gained by trading with his lord's goods to his own advantage, he has perverted the trust reposed in him"* (*Counsels on Stewardship*, p. 113).

We often sing and talk about trusting in Jesus, but we seldom stop to think about the trust Jesus has placed on us. This is a sobering thought. Jesus has entrusted us with the greatest work of all—the giving of truth to others so that they might experience and obtain eternal life in Him. This responsibility has been given to us because it is in sharing this truth that we ourselves develop characters like His and are prepared to live with Him in Heaven and the New Earth.

How Do We Become Good Stewards of the Gospel?

Jesus knew what it would take to carry out this great mission. In the light of this knowledge, He laid down the major principles that will bring success. These principles may be summarized as follows:

1. We are stewards of everything in our lives.
2. We are a community of believers with Christ as our Lord and Master, God as our Father, and the Holy Spirit as our Guide.
3. Our task is worldwide, embracing all people everywhere.
4. We are accountable to God for all, not just a fragment, of our time, talent, possessions, service—even our very lives.
5. It is the motive that determines the moral quality of our living and giving.

By following the stewardship principles outlined in God's Word, we will find a full "army" of equipped officers and workers in every local church. It will mean an interested, alert, passionate, devoted, and consecrated church membership. It will eliminate all false methods and money-raising schemes for financing the church. True stewardship principles will encourage the method of direct, systematic, and worshipful giving on the basis of a person's prosperity as the one means of support for the work of His kingdom. It will provide the buildings and material equipment needed in every locality of every country for the work at hand. It will meet the practical needs of our time for the spread of truth throughout the world. It will make possible the evangelization of every man, woman, and child in the world and, ultimately, hasten the Second Coming of Jesus Christ.

A Good and Faithful Servant

Most often in our contemporary society when the topic of success comes up, it is attached to material and financial possessions. Is that God's definition? In God's plan, it is possible for a poor person to be successful as well. Notice this from Matthew 25:21, *"His lord said to him, 'Well done, good and faithful servant; you were faithful over a few things, I will make you ruler over many things. Enter into the joy of your lord.'"*

Even our faith is a gift of God and therefore subject to the considerations of stewardship. Our faith requires faithfulness in its uses and blessings. This is substantiated in Hebrews 12:1-3, *"Therefore we also, since we are surrounded by so great a cloud of witnesses, let us lay aside every weight, and the sin which so easily ensnares us, and let us run with endurance the race that is set before us, looking unto Jesus, the author and finisher of our faith, who for the joy that was set before Him endured the cross, despising the shame, and has sat down at the right hand of the throne of God. For consider Him who endured such hostility from sinners against Himself, lest you become weary and discouraged in your souls."*

"The truth is soon to triumph gloriously, and all who now choose to be laborers together with God will triumph with it" (Testimonies for the Church, vol. 9, p. 135).

The Stewardship Vision for God's Church

It is a few years from now. Pastors and local church leaders have been successful at creating a stewardship environment in the church. They have taught, trained, supported, and encouraged the church family in Biblical financial stewardship.

People are implementing Biblical principles into their lives. They are growing in generosity, saving on a regular basis for the unexpected, and moving out from under the bondage of consumer debt.

Their lifestyles are marked by moderation, discipline, and contentment. Money has been

eliminated as the rival god, and they are growing in their relationship with the Creator God.

It is Sabbath morning and people are arriving for services.

In their countenance is a radiated joy that comes from being a generous giver. In their demeanor is a sense of peace—a lack of anxiety over financial matters, a pervading sense of contentment and gratefulness.

Marital conflict over money has been largely eliminated. The members enter worship with a sense of anticipation and expectation of God's presence and work among them.

The church's ministries are fully funded, and the church has a strong outreach globally and to the local community. It extends the love of Christ in very tangible ways to those in need.

Funds have been made available to provide church facilities that wonderfully facilitate ministry and that are maintained with excellence.

The question before leadership is, "What is God calling us to do with the abundant resources with which He has entrusted us?"

Eyes on the Prize

So, let us keep our eyes on the prize. Our hearts will be where our treasure is. The things of this earth, which are soon to be burned up, will grow strangely dim in the light of God's glory and grace. Then, as each day passes, as we near the Second Coming or the end of our lives, instead of thinking about leaving our treasures behind, we can think of our treasures in heaven and realize that we are moving closer to them. *"Your thoughts will be fixed upon the great rewards of eternity. All your plans will be made in reference to the future, immortal life. You will be drawn toward your treasure. You will not study your worldly interest; but in all your pursuits the silent inquiry will be, 'Lord, what wilt Thou have me to do?'"* (*Counsels on Stewardship*, p. 343).

Christian stewardship begins and ends with Jesus. He created everything in the beginning. He is the rightful owner. In this life we simply manage for Him. Things only become ours when we give them away—to God's cause. *"Shall we cling to our*

possessions till they fall into the hands of our enemies? The time is coming when commandment keepers can neither buy nor sell. Of what use will houses and lands, bank stock and merchandise, be to us then? <u>Now is the time to place our treasures where they will be eternally secure</u>. It is time for those who have large possessions to cut down the principal, that God's work may be extended in foreign lands. 'Sell that ye have, and give alms; provide yourselves bags which wax not old, a treasure in the heavens that faileth not, where no thief approacheth, neither moth corrupteth.' <u>That which we give to the cause of God becomes our own forever</u>. Says Christ, 'Lay up for yourselves treasures in heaven.' <u>These alone, of all that we possess, are really ours. All that we lay up on earth, we must leave at last. It is only what we give for Christ that we can take with us into the eternal world</u>" (*Review and Herald*, December 6, 1887, underlining by editor).

The journey that we have taken to understand the Christian principles of money management is drawing to a close. We started with Genesis 1:1 and we close with our eyes on Revelation 21:1-4—from Eden to Eden. *"Now I saw a new heaven and a new earth, for the first heaven and the first earth had passed away. Also there was no more sea. Then I, John, saw the holy city, New Jerusalem, coming down out of heaven from God, prepared as a bride adorned for her husband. And I heard a loud voice from heaven saying, 'Behold, the tabernacle of God is with men, and He will dwell with them, and they shall be His people. God Himself will be with them and be their God. And God will wipe away every tear from their eyes; there shall be no more death, nor sorrow, nor crying. There shall be no more pain, for the former things have passed away.'"* Let's confirm our decision to financial faithfulness. Let us keep our eyes on the prize, and let nothing distract us.

We pray that God will sustain and bless you and your family as you seek His will in this important area of your life. May we all be in the group that hears from the lips of Jesus, "Well done, good and faithful servant…enter into the joy of your Lord."

Assignment for this lesson:

1. Memorize Matthew 25:21.
2. Complete the worksheets for this lesson.
3. Make a commitment to God to be financially faithful.

The Rewards of Financial Faithfulness

Memory Verse: Matthew 25:21

"His lord said to him, 'Well done, good and faithful servant; you were faithful over a few things, I will make you ruler over many things. Enter into the joy of your lord.'"

PRAYER TIME:

Make a list of those in your group who have asked for special prayer needs this week and pray for them each day.

_____

_____

Pray also for God's wisdom and blessing as you develop your financial plan.

STUDY TIME:

Day One

Read and reflect on 1 Corinthians 4:1, 2, and 5 and Psalms 19:7-11.

1. What is the "trust" that has been given and what do you think it means to be faithful? _____

    _____

    _____

    _____

2. What is the appointed time? _____

    _____

    _____

3. How important is motive to the idea of receiving God's praise? Explain. _____

_____

_____

_____

4. What do you think is meant by the "great reward" in Psalms 19:11? _____

_____

_____

_____

Day Two:

Read and reflect on Hebrews 11:6 and Revelation 22:12.

1. Why is faith essential to pleasing God? _____

_____

_____

2. Why does God give rewards? Doesn't that cloud the motivations? Explain. _____

_____

_____

_____

3. What does it mean to earnestly seek Him? _____

_____

_____

4. What reward is Jesus bringing with Him? _____

_____

_____

5. What does it mean to you that every man will be rewarded according to what he has done? _____

_____

_____

Day Three:

Read and reflect on Revelation 14:13.

1. Why is it "blessed" to die "in the Lord?" _____

_____

_____

_____

2. Explain your understanding of "their works follow them" in this text. _____

_____

_____

_____

Read and reflect on Matthew 16:27.

3. How can the setting of the Second Coming be the time for the rewards? Shouldn't the rewards be after

the judgment? Explain. _____

_____

_____

_____

4. Since we are saved by faith, why are we rewarded according to our works? _____

_____

_____

_____

Day Four:

Read and reflect on Luke 6:22, 23 and compare with Matthew 5:11, 12.

1. Paraphrase verse 22 into your own words and understanding. _____

_____

_____

_____

_____

2. What is the day when the rejoicing is to take place? _____

_____

_____

3. What is the connection between ill-treatment, rejoicing, and reward? What is the reward that is

mentioned here? _____

_____

_____

_____

4. What is the motivation that should keep people faithful during times of adversity? _____

_____

_____

_____

Day Five:

Read and reflect on 2 Peter 1:10-11.

1. What is Peter referring to in verse 10? _____

_____

_____

_____

2. What is being suggested by the phrase "you will never fall?" _____

_____

_____

_____

3. What is your understanding of a "rich or abundant" welcome? _____

_____

_____

_____

Read and reflect on Matthew 25:19.

4. When does the lord of the servants return? What does that mean? _____

_____

_____

_____

5. How would you explain "settled accounts with them"? _____

_____

_____

_____

Day Six:

Read and reflect on Luke 14:12-14.

1. What is the suggestion of these 3 verses? _____

_____

_____

_____

2. What are you to charge for this banquet? Expand on your response. _____

_____

_____

_____

3. Is the payment mentioned here the resurrection or something else? Explain. _____

_____

_____

_____

4. Explain your reaction to learning more about the rewards prepared for the faithful. _____

_____

_____

_____

_____

_____

Bibliography

Blue, Ron. *Splitting Heirs*, Northfield Publishing, Chicago.

Burkett, Larry. *Investing for the Future*, Chariot Victor Publishing, Colorado Springs, CO.

Fithian, Scott C. *Values Based Estate Planning*, John Wiley & Sons, Inc., New York.

Holy Bible, New King James Version, Thomas Nelson Publishers, Nashville, TN.

Pryor, Austin. *Sound Mind Investing*, Third Edition, Austin Pryor, 2000.

Warren, Elizabeth, and Tyagi, Amelia Warren. *The Two Income Trap*, Basic Books, New York.

White, Ellen G. Australasian Union Conference Record

Ibid. *Bible Echo and Signs of the Times*
—. *Child Guidance*
—. *Christian Service*
—. *Christ's Object Lessons*
—. *Counsels on Health*
—. *Counsels on Stewardship*
—. *Education*
—. *Evangelism*
—. *Gospel Workers*
—. *Manuscript Releases*, vol. 4, vol. 5, vol. 20
—. *Patriarchs and Prophets*
—. *Review and Herald*
—. *Steps to Christ*
—. *Testimonies for the Church*, volumes 2, 3, 4, 5, 6, 9
—. *The Adventist Home*
—. *The Desire of Ages*
—. *The Gospel Herald*

U. S. News and World Report, February 4, 2000.